THE FAITH OF OUR FATHER

THE FAITH OF

E. P. DUTTON & CO., INC., NEW YORK, 1966

OUR FATHER

by H. Gordon Green

Contents

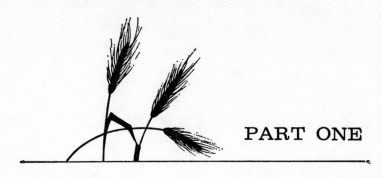

PART ONE

Before We Knew Him

Chapter 1

ESCAPING QUIETLY from the heartland of industrial Ontario is a highway which idles north to the village of Arthur. You must look for it sometime when the world seems stale. It will whisk you away from propriety and the eight-hour day as gaily as a truant might do, for here is one thoroughfare which has yet to fall in line with efficiency and strait-laced discipline. Here is a road which takes its old-fashioned time on the daisy-sloped hills, and its meanderings are still as unreasonable as those of a carefree calf. It can show you snake fences again, and grayboard barns and marshes so brimming with life that the woods beyond quiver with it.

Mind that a deer doesn't come sailing up out of the ditch at you. And mind that you don't hit a steer or an unemployed horse.

At Guelph, the post sign says, "Arthur—24 miles." But at Arthur, the sign which points backward says, "Guelph—23 miles." Ask why and you may be told, "Because, sir, it's

9

downhill to Guelph!" For in Arthur, you see, talk has an Irish tint to it.

I'd thank you to lift your hat here, because you are now in my home town, and you are talking to my people. And here, on the green rim of the village, in a little brick house which still clings like a smiling old woman to her garden, this story begins. For it was under the low roof of this house—just a few inches under it—in July of 1883, and on a day when his little wren of a mother was really much too busy to afford such an interruption, that our father was born. And it was in this house that he grew up, the seventh of the sons of Bill and Mary Ann Green—the quiet one in a bull-lunged crew that swelled to eleven.

But this book is not intended to begin with our father's boyhood, much as I would like to preserve that part of his life for those of us who will one day be so eager to bring him back. Since this is essentially *his* book, it will commence at that point of his life which he himself regards as its true beginning. Which means that it will not begin with the day when he was born, but rather with that time when, to use his own scripture for it, he was "born again."

It wasn't until 1900, in the summer of his seventeenth birthday that our father first became aware of that scripture, and truth to tell, there was nothing divinely dramatic about that awareness. The day itself was to have its share of usual adventure, but he was not struck glorious with sudden light as Paul was on the Damascus road. The day started almost like any other, with his younger brothers chasing over beds, sticking dirty toes in faces still asleep, and pulling at one another's underwear flaps while from the kitchen below came sniffs of cedar smoke and hot biscuits. Up the stairs too came their mother's shrill protests at the uproar.

But it wasn't until his mother's voice was aimed directly at him that the youth finally shook himself free of his bed. "Henry! You've got to get up now! You don't be late for your first day at a new job, you know! Leastways not for old E. J. Callaghan!"

When Henry was at the table a minute later and she was frying eggs and salt pork for him, Mary Ann had still more advice to offer. For E. J. Callaghan was the great hard man who owned the Arlington, and the Arlington was a tavern with a reputation which was quite notorious then, even for a place like Arthur.

"Just one thing I don't like about this here job of yours," she said. "It's altogether too handy to them beer pumps!"

Henry patted his mother's shoulder and told her not to worry. The job was in Callaghan's livery stable and not in his hotel, he told her, and besides he didn't have any money and he didn't even like the stuff.

His mother sighed and shook her head sadly. This wasn't the first time one of her sons had told her not to worry, and then had become a steady patron of the taproom.

"You'll have to excuse me for nagging at you, Henry," she said as she finally handed him his lunch pail that morning, "but it's just that—well, I do believe that if a Green can lick likker he can lick anything! And—and it's such a waste for folks that don't have much to begin with!"

There was a plea in her eyes that shook him a little, and he didn't know what to do about it but to kiss the top of her head and repeat his promise that she needn't worry.

At eight that morning, Mr. E. J. Callaghan led the six men he had just hired to the big livery stable back of his hotel, and there he gave careful directions as to how the new floor must be laid. At nine, with the work safely started, Callaghan left to drive a traveler out into the country. At eleven, with the July heat already smoking up the roads and blistering the tar on the roofs, Callaghan came back from his trip to find only one man still working in his stable. The rest were enduring the heat of the day in the cool of the Arlington taproom.

Was it that good-by promise he had given his mother which saved Henry from being fired along with the others that day? Or was it true, as his mother once told me when I asked her, that our father was always different from his brothers? That he was always the quiet one? And was there any connection between that hasty promise—or between the stern lesson Mr. Callaghan administered that day on the wages of sin—and what our father did later that same day? Would he have had the necessary conscience anyhow?

For even as our father bent to his work in the cement again that morning, an ambassador of destiny was slowly approaching on the Guelph road.

To the farmers who nodded a cautious greeting that day, the solitary stranger in that northbound buggy must have been very puzzling. He was tall, spare, and with a pale stern face half covered with dense black beard. His hat was the "Christie-stiff" derby peculiar to the day, and his black suit, though plain, was certainly not that of a worker. But apart from the curious intensity of the restless eyes the most unusual feature of the man was the fact that he wore no tie, an omission which at first glance gave one the impression that here was surely a clergyman from some fashionable church in one of the prosperous towns to the south.

Clergyman he was too, though certainly not of any of the properly established denominations. Nor did his refusal to wear a tie stem from any desire to give himself the appearance thereof. He wore his collar without decoration, simply because the apostle Paul had very clearly warned of the sin of adorning the outer man. A necktie was adornment; and it must have given this strange traveler with the burning Old Testament eyes no small embarrassment to realize that to leave it off as Paul had commanded made him look as if he were wearing the Roman collar affected by those clerics whose degrees and lukewarm orthodoxy he so utterly spurned.

It was also clear that the traveler had been on the road for a long time, for the mud which was baked onto the wheel rims of his buggy often showed colors that were quite different from the sour gray clay of Wellington County. Furthermore, the sack of oats which was roped across the back of the buggy was now nearly empty.

The front of the vehicle, however, was so heavily loaded with boxes and suitcases that the driver scarcely had sitting space. What no one could have guessed was how very little of self those suitcases contained, for instead of clothes and personal possessions they were filled with tracts, religious books and several thousand copies of a magazine called *The Gospel Trumpet.*

Noon brought the prophet's slow and slightly limping horse over the iron bridge below Arthur, thence up the steep grade which led to the head of Main Street and to the rambling three-storied brick structure which, in curly-tailed lettering, proudly announced itself as "The Arlington." A pack of deerhounds came out from the hotel to meet the stranger as he tied up to the hitching post, and a couple of tattered, unshaven graybeards looked at him with mild curiosity through their pipe smoke.

"Nelson is my name," the man said as he came up to them. "Do you suppose I could find lodging here until I get someone to put a front shoe on that horse of mine?"

The two old fellows looked at each other and without any verbal consultation agreed that this might be possible. "Mr. Callaghan runs this here hotel, sir," one of them told him. "Jes' go in an' ask for E.J."

By this time the first ratgnaw of doubt about the place had already begun to take hold of the traveler. The strong stale smell of beer had now reached through the hot dust of the road to him, and from within the cool dark of the big room on the left came the unmistakable sounds of lusty argument, sharply emphasized by lewd oaths or the slamming of glasses on the table.

Harry Nelson hesitated, his head tilted up slightly as if pausing to ask the Lord for guidance. "Perhaps," he said finally to the two old men in the sun, "I better look after my horse first. Could you direct me to a good blacksmith? But I'd have to find a smith that wouldn't try to take advantage of me. I'm not a commercial man, you know. I'm just an evangelist."

At this peculiar word the two pipes came down together. "A who, sir?"

"An evangelist," Mr. Nelson repeated, picking up a slightly fierce pride now. "A Johnny Appleseed of the gospel, come all the way from Indiana to preach the true word of God!"

Somewhere during Nelson's proclamation of his high calling, Henry Green came up from the livery stable to eat his lunch by the pump, there to fall under the spell of this strange man's fervor.

The old men seemed as perplexed by the stranger as Henry was. "And just what faith might you subscribe to, sir?" one of them asked.

This was always a difficult question for Mr. Nelson, for his allegiance was to none of the regular denominations. He was, in fact, unshakably convinced that church membership could be a snare and a delusion, and with more courage than discretion he told them why. A man needed to be sure of his crown of glory, he said, by being born again. What was more, he was certain that the churches of the day were often apt to hinder that rebirth rather than to preach it. Such a theology could not be fully explained right here and now, but Mr. Nelson did have a neat, sure summary of his belief which he always kept at the ready.

"Let's just say that mine is the 'faith once delivered unto the saints.' "

To the two graybeards that vague reference to the saints at least allowed them to guess at his correct religious classification. "Sure now and if it's Catholic you be," said one of them, "why don't ye see Father Doherty before ye do anythin' else. Sure an' himself's a great horseman too! He might be right glad to help you out!"

Mr. Nelson soon let it be known that he was most certainly not to be associated with the church of Rome.

"Aha!" said the other man, glad that they had now surely come to the end of this embarrassing mystery. After all, there were only two kinds of religions that had to do with saints, weren't there? "Just like I figured all along, Jake. It's George Buschlen you ought to see! George is not only the best blacksmith in town but he do be summat of a preacher man himself. Same breed as you, I reckon. Latter-day Saint, I take it?"

The evangelist from Indiana sighed and shook his head hopelessly. "No and I'm most certainly not a Latter-day Saint either! I'm an *every-day* saint!"

Just as it seemed that Nelson might begin to exhort again, one of the simmering arguments within the saloon suddenly rose past the boiling point. There was the splat of a fist smashing flesh, a table turned turtle and the sounds of blasphemy and spilling beer. Then the door swung open and a stout lad, his face red with sun and anger, his trunk writhing with furious protest, was carried out like a bag of grist. Once outside, the victim redoubled his efforts and as he was carried past the evangelist he gave such a violent twist that one of the four stalwarts carrying him was thrown against Nelson so forcibly it almost up-ended him.

"Sorry us pallbearers got to be so undignified, sir," the man excused himself. "But our corpse ain't altogether dead yet!"

Without pausing for further explanation, the "pall-bearers" now went around the front corner of the hotel and headed for the low frame shop on the other side of the yard between.

"There now, reverend," one of the old men said, pointing to the scaling sign which said "Campbell & Fair—Blacksmithing & Carpentry," "you were asking for a man to shoe your horse, I believe. Well you just follow those silly galoots now, because that's 'zactly where they be goin'."

"The blacksmith's just the other side of that big tub of water, sir," Henry offered.

Dumfounded, Nelson watched the four men as they dropped their thrashing burden with a mighty splash into the blacksmith's tub.

"In this town, sir," Henry explained, "it comes in handy for a hotel to have a blacksmith right next door."

"Brutal!" Nelson muttered half under his breath. "I've never, never seen anything like it!"

"Oh, there's lots of guys around here that's got cooled off in the sobering tub, sir," Henry said as the man who had just been dunked got to his feet.

The man who had begged Nelson's pardon came back now to apologize further. "Sorry, mister, but we just couldn't shut that guy up today! He was one of those young lads that set fire to the bandstand last February when we got word that Ladysmith was relieved—"

"Ladysmith? . . . Relieved? . . . " Nelson repeated cautiously.

"Ladysmith! Down in the South African War, you know! Where all them there women and children and all was bein' penned up and starved to death by them Boers!" The man looked at the evangelist severely. "Don't tell me you never heard of Ladysmith!" he said.

Come to think of it, Harry Nelson had heard of this war which was going on between the British and the Boers, though he really didn't see how it could be so very important without his own country taking part.

"Well, siree!" the man went on, "you know the magistrate let those guys off easy for settin' fire to that bandstand. Crazy business anyways, tryin' to celebrate a victory by burnin' the only bandstand in town! Magistrate only fined him twenty dollars but this lad just can't forget it! Thinks he's been outraged or somethin'. . . . Well now, mister, we just can't have people in our favorite tavern who are as disrespectful of the law as that!"

Harry Nelson made a noise in his nose that cut the speech short.

"Guess you don't approve of the way we do things around here," the man said in a tone which invited a crowd to gather behind him. "That right, mister?"

"No," Nelson said very quietly, "I do not approve!"

The man turned around to consult with his cohorts and with those who were just beginning to gather. He said, "What do you know? Here's a stranger come to town and already he don't like the way we do things! You better advise me on this, boys!"

Turning again to Nelson, he came a nose closer and asked, "Where you from anyhow, bud? You sound awful important to be in a place like Arthur. You sound almost as important as an American or something!"

"I am an American," Nelson told them, still very calm. "And I doubt if that calls for any apology!"

The crowd began to push closer.

"And what are you doin' here? What's your business?"

"I happen to be an evangelist, gentlemen."

"A what? What's that ten-gallon word you just said?"

"I'm an evangelist."

Henry said, "He means that he's a sort of preacher."

One of those so recently arrived from the taproom that he still walked as if aboard ship—he was one of the cement workers Callaghan had fired a few hours before—now pushed his way into the circle. "Well now," he said, "we sure do stand in need of a preacher, mister. How about givin' us a sample of your wares? Okay, lads?"

"If he's a preacher how come he don't approve of what we did to Paddy there?" someone else wanted to know. "Sure we were just baptizing him!"

"Let's take him over to the front of the hotel! The front steps would make a good enough pulpit!"

Somewhere in the crowd a hand reached out as if to take

Nelson's shoulder, but it never quite reached. "If you think you're going to make a fool of me," said Nelson, "you're quite mistaken." And there was something in the way he said it and in the steady, superior way he dared their eyes that made them hesitate.

"Nor am I going to mount the steps of any tavern to preach the Word of God," he went on. "But for those of you who wish a sermon, I have one nevertheless. In fact I have a hundred pounds of sermons in my buggy over there. Come, I'll show you!"

But at the buggy the man who had been so determined to have a free sermon regained some of his courage. "Never mind all the bleedin' literchure, parson," he said as he tossed a fistful of tracts at the sky. "What give you the idea that we could read anyways? Now just git up there in that there buggy of yours and talk about temptation or something. Come on! Up you git!"

It was Callaghan, once again arriving when least expected, who put an end to the scene, and Callaghan was still apologizing for the lack of civilization in his town when Harry Nelson finally clicked to his horse to limp along a little further. He had intended paying a visit to "Campbell & Fair," but he knew better than that now.

"Thanks for one more deliverance, Lord!" he murmured as he went down the main street; and then, making sure that he didn't let himself become critical, he fell to wondering what strange purpose the Lord must have had in mind when He brought him to such a den of iniquity as the Arlington. "Would to God," he prayed, "that these people were as concerned about their eternal souls as they are about making jokes and their drinking and their banty rooster wars and their funny British laws!"

Just as Nelson was about to turn the corner at the foot of

the main street, he was surprised to see a youth running after him and waving him to stop.

"Thought I might save you a little trouble," the boy panted. "When you were looking the other way one of those fellows at the hotel twisted this nut off your wheel back there. I picked it up. You wouldn't have gone far without losing yourself a wheel, sir."

When the nut was secure again, Harry Nelson was so grateful for the favor that he took out his slender wallet and tried to pay for it.

"It's nothing, sir, but I just didn't see any point in a good buggy getting all busted up and all those books being spread over the road."

"And what did you say your name was?"

"Henry Green, sir. I was working back of the hotel today."

"Lord bless you, Henry. Lord bless you and keep you!"

It was a peculiar way to thank a man, Henry thought. Made a guy uncomfortable. Maybe he should have taken the money instead.

"Do you read, Henry?"

"Yes, sir."

"Well then, I've got a magazine for you—one you haven't seen before. We call it *The Gospel Trumpet*. I do hope you read it carefully, Henry, and Lord bless you again!"

Late that same afternoon, Harry Nelson's buggy full of "gospel seed" pulled up in the shade of a hardwood grove some eight miles east of Arthur on the second concession of a township bearing the hopeful name of Luther. His horse was now limping so badly that Nelson knew he had no choice but to find a place for the night. But as he got down from his buggy to ease the cramps from his legs, he kept looking at the grove beyond the rail fence.

"What a perfectly beautiful bit of woodland!" he said to himself. "So open and clean! Right beside a school and a store corner too! What a marvelous place it would be for a country camp meeting!"

A tall, intelligent-looking farmer who seemed unusually friendly stopped his team of magnificent Clydesdales just as Nelson was feeding his own horse the last of the oats. "Hot day," he said.

"Didn't think it would get so hot up here," Nelson replied. "Does this place have a name?"

"Hasn't got much else," the farmer replied. "But it does have a name. Name of Pepabun. Kind of silly for a name, wouldn't you say?"

It took only a few minutes to get acquainted with a farmer like this. His name was Lucas—Abner Lucas—and he lived in the brick house just back on the right.

"My name is Harry Nelson and I'm a preacher with a horse that's thrown a shoe. Would you by any chance know someone around here who could put it back on for me?"

"You've got the shoe?"

"Right here. Hung over the footrung."

Abner Lucas took the shoe and looked at it briefly. "Come on up to supper!" he invited. "I'll have that on in two shakes of a dead lamb's tail!"

"I don't think I should, really. I—I—"

"You say you're a preacher man? Well, you know my wife will be just awful glad to see you! We've got at least three youngsters up there that ought to be christened. Just never got around to it, you know, being so far away from any church and all."

The evangelist shook his head with a sad smile. "I'll be

very sorry to disappoint your wife," he said, "but my people don't believe in baby sprinkling. We believe in baptism by immersion."

Such theological details were of little importance to Abner Lucas then. "Come along anyways!" he repeated. "I know the wife will sure be glad to see you no matter whether you sprinkle, dip or just say 'Amen' when it rains! . . . Mind now that you give your horse his time crossing my culvert up here. It's awful shaky. . . ."

Back home in Arthur that evening, Henry's father listened to the story of the preacher from Indiana at the supper table and decided that he didn't care for the man. "Can't feel sorry for him at all," he said. "Can't feel sorry for any man that won't do a man's work."

But Henry said, "They didn't have to be so mean to him. He just came looking for a blacksmith. That shouldn't have made them act like a bunch of savages."

"Well," Bill said, "when one of these Americans wants something, it isn't patriotic for him to ever give up. And when one of them comes to Canada looking for savages to missionary to, I think savages ought to be provided. Sorry I wasn't in on the fun myself, kind of."

"You wouldn't have got any more fun out of him than anyone else," Henry told him. "Because there's one man even you couldn't scare. Not even with your best swearing you couldn't."

Bill blew his tea so hard it jumped. "Now there's a man I'll just have to meet someday," he said.

In his bed that night, Henry unrolled *The Gospel Trumpet* and held it up to the lamp. But he couldn't really get interested in it.

Chapter 2

THE CHURCH WAS built in 1904, but not all the cheerful givers who pointed it skywards that spring were numbered with the newly ransomed. Many who came to help with the work were merely friends out to enjoy the jollity which always went with such an occasion, and to gorge themselves on the bountiful baking which the women were sure to provide.

There was little resentment toward this new belief. It was true that Harry Nelson's saints were different. They didn't drink; they didn't smoke; they didn't play cards or dance. Their yeas were yeas and their nays were nays, with never a hint of rougher words added for variety. The converts were dipped in the muddy waters of the Conestoga creek, sang their hymns to the clapping of hands or the whanging of guitars. Their services were long and unbelievably noisy too, and these people were never content to let their minister do their praying for them: everyone took his turn. And if the contribution had to hang suspended in midair sometimes for lack of courage or the right words, it didn't really matter. There were so many amens and hallelujahs rising up from the rest of the congregation that no one but God Himself would notice the trouble.

These were things which were more apt to draw quiet smiles than indignation from the outsiders, however. Besides, the Canadian farm country was still languishing then in that unprogressive age when one could alway afford the time to be neighborly.

So there were sinners too with the builders that spring, and among them were Bill Green, and his twenty-one-year-old son, Henry. They drove up one morning in a spavined light wagon, just as the workers had finished the foundation and were wondering uncomfortably how best to lay the first big timbers. Bill had come all the way from town that morning, but he had picked up his son just two miles down the concession at the Stuckeys, where Henry had been working as a hired hand cutting wood all that winter.

"Lay off that beam before you commit a monstrosity!" Bill commanded as he moved at once to take charge. "Here, let me show you how to do it! Old Jim Fuller sure was right when he told me you'd be in the soup with this raising unless someone got you started straight. . . ."

Harry Nelson, the man who could generally look at a man and see clear down to the gravel of his soul, was as puzzled by Bill Green's character now as he had been when he had first met him just four years ago. "Well, Mr. Green," he smiled finally, "we certainly wouldn't want to build on sinking sand, would we? But tell me, how come you've come all the way out here from Arthur this morning? I mean—well, we really can't pay you, you know!"

"Oh, don't worry about that, Reverend!" Bill said, whipping a chain around the end of a 40-foot timber. "I know better than to expect money from a church that thinks gold is the root of all evil. . . . Henry! Henry! Slack off on that guy wire! . . . No, Reverend, I'm just here to do an old friend of mine a favor. You mind Jim Fuller that used to live down the road there a ways? Well he's moved to Arthur now. Sick, he is. Eat up with cancer and going to die. I guess you know that though, don't you? Sure you would. . . . Well, old Jim just can't get this church off his mind. Wanted to have something to do with it, you see, and it can't be money of course. . . . Slack off, Henry, slack off, I said!"

Bill added an oath which split the air and made Harry Nelson try to protest, but he pretended to notice none of the discomfort his picturesque vocabulary was causing.

". . . And I just felt so sorry for the old boy I told him I'd come out here and do his bit for him. So you tell the Lord to chalk this one up to Jim Fuller's account, will you? I owe him a turn or two anyways. . . . Henry! . . . Why don't you slack off!!"

This time the oath was so shocking that Harry Nelson flinched. "Please, Mr. Green!" he begged. "Please don't dishonor the name of the Lord that way! Especially on a job so sacred as this one!"

Bill Green lifted his sweaty cap and wrinkled his red face with an embarrassed look which he most certainly did not feel.

"Excuse me for two weeks, Reverend!" Bill said. "I guess I just wasn't thinking! Well now, I suppose I just better bring that sort of talk to a cease, eh? Okay, Reverend, I'll just try to do that! . . ."

At the other end of the freshly built basement, Henry

was doing his best to give the big guy pole a more business-like anchoring than it had had when his father had taken over. Henry was a rather short lad, wiry and well built, and he worked with the quick, sure movements of one who knows exactly what he wants to do. He had worked with his father ever since he could lace himself into a man's boots and he needed little direction now. He was a shy, good-looking lad who seldom flustered, and it didn't bother him at all to have his father shout commands at him when he was already doing his best. Besides, he knew his father's kind of humor well enough to realize that there was a reason beyond that of supervising for all the yelling which was now aimed at him.

"Henry! What in the Devil . . . ?"

Harry Nelson's face suddenly took on the severity of the prophet. "Mr. Green!" he said sharply, "I just will not have your using language like that!"

Bill Green straightened up from his work and pretended absolute surprise, but mischief was in his eyes. "I'm sorry, Reverend," he said, "but I just don't get this at all. A minute ago you told me to lay off those other words I was saying. Well now, I ask you, Reverend, does your church figure it's a sin to dishonor the Devil too?"

Harry Nelson coughed and managed a kindly smile. Henry looked out across the fields and wished his father wouldn't tease like this.

"Not meaning to make fun of you, Reverend, but you'd think you had the Devil by the tail and was jabbing him with his own pitchfork! I just never met up with a religion in all my life that was so bent on booting the Devil back to hell! And now you want me to keep the old buzzard's name sort of sacred like!"

Harry Nelson smiled in a sadly sympathetic way. "Mr.

Green," he said, putting a fatherly hand on Bill's shoulder, "there must be many of our beliefs which are somewhat curious to you. But you know every one of them would be as clear as crystal to you if you would only let the Lord open your eyes for you. . . . Bill—you don't mind if I call you Bill, do you?—Bill, why don't you come to worship with us? The Lord could certainly use a man with your energy, if you'd only let Him lead you!"

"I'd give the Lord so much trouble He'd have no time left for anyone else!" Bill laughed, bending to his work again.

"But, Bill!" Harry Nelson said, his hand going again to the hard shoulder, and his eyes lighting with the dark, fierce fires of complete conviction, "have you ever really thought about it?"

When Bill straightened up this time, the laugh had disappeared. "Yes, I have, Reverend. And I guess that's why the church and me don't have nothing much to say to each other."

"You don't believe?"

Bill wasn't quite sure that he wanted to answer.

"It's an awful thing not to believe, Bill!" Harry Nelson said, and there was something so ominous in the way he said it that those around them began hushing one another to listen. Nelson moved closer and dropped his voice as he might have done in the valley of one of his Sunday-night prayers. "In all the world, Bill," he said, "there is nothing so utterly awful as to disbelieve! Because there's nothing so utterly awful as to be lost, Bill! Lost! Lost! . . . Is there any sadder word in all the language, Bill?"

Bill Green had a quick reply. "Do you think the good Lord would send me to hell for something I couldn't do?"

Harry Nelson tightened the brotherly arm around Bill Green's wide shoulders. "Bill," he said, "as the Good Book says, there are many things about God that we see only through a glass, darkly. But there are at least two things about Him which are never in doubt. He is a just God, and He is also a merciful one. . . . No indeed, Bill, the Lord isn't going to send you to hell for something you can't do!"

"Well, Reverend, I just can't *believe!* And a minute ago you told me that was the surest way to hell there was! There's just something about this argument that I'm not smart enough to understand!"

Harry Nelson's arm dropped in limp disappointment. "Oh, Bill!" he said fervently, "but you *could* believe if you only wanted to! It would be so easy! And so divinely wonderful!"

Bill put both hands into his overalls pockets. "I'd like to believe these pockets were full of ten-buck bills!" he said suddenly pulling both pockets inside out. "Do you really think I can? Just by wanting to, I mean?"

Harry Nelson sighed deeply. How did one go about convincing someone with a sinner's scales on his eyes that you could not compare the unsearchable riches of the Almighty with a dirty pair of empty pockets? "Bill," he said with the kindest laugh in the world, "I'm sure going to be praying for you!

"God's so powerful, Bill, that He can do absolutely anything! As the Good Book says, He has the power to move the hardest heart or the highest mountain! There is just nothing that He couldn't do, Bill."

"Could He make a stone so big that He couldn't lift it, Reverend?"

For a moment it seemed that Harry Nelson had at last

been confronted with a theological problem for which he had no ready answer. And while Henry and the other volunteer workers gathered close to follow this debate through to its conclusion, Bill had still another question to ask. It was a question which he asked with a flare of emotion that was rather surprising to those who knew him best.

"You say your God can do absolutely anything, Reverend! And you say too that He is full of love and mercy. Now I ask you, if He's able to do anything He wants, why doesn't He do something to help out all this here suffering that's going on in the world? . . . You might think you've heard some pretty powerful praying in your day, but you haven't heard anything in all your life like a mother praying for a kid that's choking to death in front of her! And my Mary Ann had to watch two of her kids go that way! Two at once! . . . Now I ask you, Reverend, where was the love of God that day?"

No one was working now. It was suddenly so quiet that even the birds seemed nervous. Harry Nelson closed his eyes for a second and his lips moved in private prayer. "Bill," he said finally in a voice which was no longer fired with the thunder of a prophet, "there are some things in this life which will always be a mystery to us. Why? Well, I guess that's just the way the Lord wants it to be, that's all! But I'm as sure as I can be, Bill, that when we get over on the other side someday we'll see all of the reasons clear as can be! And we'll wonder why in the world we ever worried about them down here! I—I just pray God that you make that shore, Bill. . . ."

The flush of anger was still on Bill's face as he met Harry Nelson's soul-searching eyes. "How *can* you be so sure?" he asked. "So sure you've got the truth, the whole truth and nothing but the truth, and everybody else is blind?"

Again came the brotherly arm and the kindly light in the preacher's face. "The truth of God isn't always something that you can perceive with reasoning alone, Bill. No indeed! You've got to perceive it spiritually!"

Bill slid away from the arm and rested the hook on the timber at his feet. "Funny thing," he said, "the last man that ever latched on to my soul like this was Father Doherty, the Catholic priest down in Arthur, and if I made him out right, that was how he got to be so sure too!"

They had had enough of this talk now, Bill thought, so with a whoop and a holler he scattered the workers and began assigning jobs. "Come on! Come on!" he shouted. "I can't stay here forever! You guys are all getting paid for this! You're laying up gold bullion in heaven for every minute you work here! So let's get this thing organized so I can get out of here! . . ."

Harry Nelson agreed that there seemed little point in further exhortation or argument, but he did think that a bit of good singing might restore them all to a mood which was more in keeping with this godly occasion, so he led them off in several stirring hymns.

> Will your anchor hold in the storms of life
> When the clouds unfold their wings of strife?
> When the strong tides lift and the cables strain
> Will your anchor shift, or firm remain?
>
> We have an anchor that keeps the soul
> Steadfast and sure while the billows roll,
> Fastened to the Rock which cannot move,
> Grounded firm and deep in the Savior's love.

Harry Nelson had hundreds of such songs in his reper-
toire, and for most of them he knew all the words of every
verse. He had a good voice, one which had the rare talent
of being able to command without any trace of harshness
creeping into its music. And he led them now in one glory
song after the other—songs that made the feet want to keep
time with the throb of the soul, songs that made you so
happy to be with the ransomed that you had to lift up your
face with the ecstasy of it, songs that made you long so
much for the better land that you could hardly keep back
the tears. . . .

And some of the songs were little more than a passage of
Scripture or a Psalm set to a simple tune.

The Lord is my Shepherd, no want shall I know;
I feed in green pastures, safe folded I rest:
He leadeth my soul where the still waters flow;
Restores me when wandering, redeems when oppressed.

There was a lull when the faithful had finished the
singing of this last song, and Bill, who had been working
without letup all this time, now paused to make his own
contribution to the program.

"Yes, yes, yes!" he said. "Very beautiful! Beautiful!
. . ."

There was little but work for the rest of that day. The
timbers were lowered into place, joined and pegged. The
bents were framed on top of them and then thrust into the
sky with a mighty "Yo! Heave!" and the red-faced straining of every ounce of man assembled. And in no time at
all, the rugged bare ribs of the frame were being clad with
new lumber.

Bill watched every operation, his tireless voice always
above all the other noises of industry. And late that after-

noon he seemed at last to be satisfied. "All right," he said, "she'll stand now. She'll be here a long time after the rest of us have gone to see whether this here preacher knows what he's talking about or not! She's so strong you couldn't ruin her now if you tried. So I can go home now, boys. . . ."

"And you think we can get her finished in time for the camp meeting?" Harry Nelson asked, after he had tried to thank Bill.

"Unless all your 'saints' start backsliding, she will!"

"We *would* like to see you come to the camp meeting, Bill. Will you come?"

Bill shook his head. "Don't count on it, Reverend."

"But just to see the dedication, Bill?"

"I don't think so, Reverend. I'm just not that kind of a man, I guess. And I don't think I ever will be. Thanks just the same."

Harry Nelson sighed. He looked over at the light wagon where Bill's horse was impatient to be off. It occurred to him then that though he had concentrated a great deal of effort on Bill all day, he had scarcely noticed this quiet young son of his. Come to think of it, he hadn't said a word to him.

"Henry!" Nelson called, "Henry, *you'll* be coming to camp meeting, won't you? There's a special invitation for you, you know."

Henry carefully studied the head of a sledge he was about to throw in the wagon, and that slight hesitation was enough to bring Harry Nelson hurrying to his side. "Oh, but we'd like to see you there!" he said. "Wouldn't you come?"

Henry tossed the sledge into the wagon. "I might," he said.

And in that second of decision was the real beginning of this story. For Henry Green was to become our father, the man whose calm but shining faith has led me to write this book.

Chapter 3

THE CAMP MEETING in 1904 was a ten-day affair, and though the raw new church was now duly dedicated to the glory of God, all but the Sunday services were held in the "brush arbor" which had been erected in the adjoining grove. This curious structure was made on the first morning of the meeting simply by butting long green poles into the earth in two vertical lines about 30 feet apart and bending both rows of the supple tops inward till they could be lashed fast to each other to make an arch. All that remained after that was to sheathe this framework everywhere with a thick covering of evergreen boughs, build a platform inside for the preacher and the singers, cover the ground with fresh sawdust, hang some lanterns, and arrange plank benches for those who were about to open their hearts to the searching of Almighty God.

The very crudity of such a tabernacle was its greatest asset, for it attracted many who would never have dared

34

the dignified and properly accredited churches of the town. So when the brush arbor was ready that year and the word got around that a famous evangelistic team had come all the way from the States, strangers who scarcely knew how to pronounce the name of the place were suddenly asking the direction to Pepabun.

As for the regular attendants themselves, most of them came to the grove joyfully prepared to camp for the entire meeting. They would pitch a tent, equip it with a straw-filled tick, blankets and provisions, and quite apart from the spiritual refreshment offered, their families would begin a July vacation whose adventures would be remembered for a lifetime.

The strangers, however, often came for only a service or two, generally driving their buggies down the concession about sundown and tying them to the trees at the edge of the grove. But they came in such numbers that before the week was over the brush arbor had to be lengthened to accommodate them all.

Some people were merely curious, or in search of free entertainment. Some came because they liked the kind of music which invited them to keep time with their feet and let their voices roll out as if no one were listening. Some came because this was the kind of faith which they had known in childhood and which, for all their effort to be reasonable, they had never quite been able to outgrow. And some came because they were young and tender and still in the darkly troubled time of their growing, when they were instinctively drawn to any voice which declared itself to be Light.

And among the latter came Henry Green, twenty-one, and as quiet and doubting as his father was boisterous and sure. He rode down to the grove that first evening with the

Stuckeys, the neighbors up the road where he was then hired boy; and he came already trembling a little at the awful magnitude of the decision which he knew he must take before this meeting was over. It was a choice which he wished he could have been spared, for he was still torn between two vehemently opposite convictions.

He stood that night with the crowd of noisy and irreverent young men who clustered at the back of the arbor because they thought they would be close enough to see all of the excitement, yet safely beyond the range of the fervent soul-searching within. He stayed there through all of the wonderful singing, and managed to smile at the jests made by some of the more worldly youths beside him about the charms of certain young women in the choir. When Harry Nelson's prayer got so long and full of burden that some small children began to wail with him, Henry kept his head unbowed and his eyes wide open.

"Isn't that old Dave Blair's girl up there with the soprano women?" asked a red-bearded lad behind him. "Wonder what old Dave thinks of that now, him a big shot and a Presbyhooligan and all!"

"Presbyhooligan or not, I say he's got one well-stacked daughter on his hands!"

Henry knew that Irish accent without turning to trace it to its source. It belonged to Tim McGuigan whose dad owned the farm just back of the Stuckey place. He despised the lad. Tim was lazy; he told tales about people; he was as crooked as a dog's hind leg. Henry had had more than one argument with him already, and to hear Tim making a remark about a girl who had been in the secret places of his heart for some time now was almost more than Henry could stand. One of these days when the time was ripe, he would get Tim in a corner and put a fist in his mouth.

Henry looked up toward the platform again, let his eyes stay on Jeannie Blair with the blue eyes and the dark hair. He would have been embarrassed beyond endurance if she should find it out right now, but someday he intended to try his luck at courting that girl—someday when he was ready, and when he was worthy enough. Jeannie was the most beautiful girl he had ever seen, he thought—so beautiful that it made him wince with anguish just to realize how utterly hopeless such a quest might be.

But even the contemplation of hate and of love couldn't keep Henry from being drawn by the terrible attraction in the gathering tension of the meeting itself. The prayers, the triumphant testimonies and the singing of the exultant glory songs were all ended now; and Harry Nelson arose to introduce the evangelist whom God had sent them all the way from Indiana. The evangelist was a balding man with a full black beard. He was a small man really, but as you watched Brother G. P. Tasker you didn't notice his stature. You saw nothing but the sharp challenge of his face and the command of his eyes.

"The Lord has anointed Brother Tasker with fire!" Harry Nelson declared. "Glory be to God! Now let the fire fall on us too!"

But Brother Tasker started gently, even smiling and telling an innocent joke. And when he read the scripture text laid upon his heart that evening, his reading was as dignified as if he had been a downtown minister. At first only his curious American accent made him seem different. He had prepared no sermon, he told them. He had no notes, nor any sure knowledge of the words that the Lord would give him.

But his restraint was short-lived. He brought the wrath

of God from the skies and poured it out on the Devil and all his works, and as he painted the glowing horrors of the hell which surely awaited the unredeemed, Henry pulled his shoulders together as if a lash were over him.

"His yoke is easy: His burden is light!" Brother Tasker declared. "When you have the Spirit dwelling within you, you don't have to worry any more about what is right and what is wrong! The next time you try to take a chaw of that tobacco plug, it just won't taste right! The next time you're invited to a dance or a card party, you just won't want to go because the Spirit will tell you that this is sin! Oh, brothers and sisters, when you've got the Spirit, you'll *hate* sin! But that's *all* you will hate. Because your soul will be filled with a love such as you've never known before. . . ."

Henry wet his lips and tried to keep his eyes off the ground. He looked around at the mottoes hanging behind some of the lanterns along the arbor's walls. Sometimes the spelling was bad and the letters very crude, but the message of each was crystal clear. *Sin Can Never Enter There! . . . The Wages of Sin Is Death . . . Ye Must Be Born Again.* All around the arbor the mottoes pointed their grim warnings at him. In the front, someone had hung a Union Jack and a Canadian Ensign. Henry tried to center his attention on them, and when that failed he tried to study the choir. But he couldn't even keep his thoughts on Jeannie Blair now. He had to look at Brother Tasker. Henry felt somehow as if the preacher were talking directly to him.

"Well," Henry tried to answer his boiling conscience, "I guess I'll make the surrender sometime, but not tonight!"

"This may be your last chance, friends!" Brother Tasker

was telling them. "By the time another camp meeting rolls around, some of us will be missing, and if you are among them, how will it be with your soul?"

Brother Tasker leaned over the pulpit, his eyes searching out the ones who were not sure. Then he looked out over the crowd toward the group outside. "You to whom God is so strange and faraway that you're even afraid to come within the sound of His voice, come home to Him tonight."

The sermon was over. Now came the singing and the pleading.

"Won't you come, boys?" Harry Nelson invited quietly. "Henry! How about it?"

Henry's throat was too full to answer. He could only shake his head. Henry looked up at the choir. There were friends in that choir who were once no better than he was right now. Why did they have to be so happy and he so wretched? Then he looked at Jeannie Blair. It was foolish for him to think he could ever be worthy of a girl like that without first straightening himself up so he could live the decent life you were supposed to. The way he was now, he couldn't even say grace at the table. Then he thought of the rambunctious, irreligious family he had come from and the way his father delighted in making fun of meetings like this.

"I could never, never be like these people in the choir!" he decided. "It might be all right for them, but this old-time religion isn't for me!"

"It was good for Paul and Silas," they sang.

Henry noticed that the young people in the choir lifted their faces as if they had found an opening in the roof of the arbor that let them look into heaven itself. The glory was fairly beaming in their faces.

"All right!" Henry decided suddenly. "I'll go. I'll go up front!"

But just as he was about to force his feet into that first fateful step, Tim spoke up behind him. "That's good music! A man could dance to that!"

Henry's dramatic decision abruptly wilted and died. He had forgotten that Tim and the other fellows were still here. "I'll *never* put on a show for them!" he told himself. "They'd laugh at me for the rest of my life! It can't be while Tim McGuigan is around to make wisecracks!"

The song went on, verse after verse.

Henry could stand no more. He walked with quick resolute step to the front and dropped to his knees beside the other penitents. The fellows could laugh at him all they wanted, but no laughing was going to keep him from gaining heaven!

When Henry was on his feet again with the great surrender made, he felt good and clean and wonderfully light. He ran over to the Stuckeys and they shook hands with him, and Charlie Stuckey put a fatherly arm about his neck. It was all over now. No more struggling within. The Devil had been rebuked. He could sing with the others.

"Makes me love everybody!" the song was rejoicing as Henry went out of the arbor to wait for the Stuckeys to load into their wagon.

All the way home that night, the endless verses of that "It's the Old-time Religion" rolled around in Henry's mind. And to give expression to the new music in his heart, he began quietly to sing it to himself. He sang all the verses he could remember, sang them over and over, but after a while whenever he came to the part which began "Makes me love everybody," something began to trouble him.

"I still can't love that Tim McGuigan!" he was thinking fiercely. And he knew that the very first time Tim made any sarcastic remark about his getting religion, he would be more apt to swat him than ever.

Was something wrong? Or did all this neighbor-loving come over you gradually?

Harry Nelson stopped in at the Stuckeys that night for a late bite and to congratulate the new convert. "That was a fine thing you did tonight, Henry! We're proud of you and so is the Lord!"

Henry felt awkward and didn't say anything.

"Makes a fellow feel a lot better, doesn't it?" Harry Nelson went on.

"Yeh. Guess it does, all right," Henry replied. "Only—"

Harry Nelson was suddenly very anxious. "Only what?"

Henry thought carefully. "Only you know when they sing that verse that says 'Makes me love everybody'—well, I just don't feel right about it. There are some folks I just can't love no matter how hard I try!"

Harry Nelson was disappointed and very concerned. "Who is it you can't love, son?"

"Tim McGuigan."

"What is there about Tim that makes you dislike him?"

It was hard for Henry to put into words. "Well," he said, "he's just no good. He makes fun of me all the time and he fights with me. And besides, I know it was Tim that swiped my crosscut out of the bush last week."

"But, Henry! Are you going to let something as small as a crosscut saw stand between you and your peace of mind?" Harry Nelson asked tensely.

Henry felt queer again. "Oh, it wasn't just the crosscut. Besides, I evened that up on my own account. I swiped his ax next day."

And now Nelson knew precisely what had to be done. "Henry," he said, "you've got to make that thing right. You've got to go to Tim and give back that ax!"

Henry quailed at the very thought of such a humiliating thing. "Oh, Mr. Nelson!" he begged. "I just can't do that! You don't understand. If it were anybody but Tim—"

"That's the only way, Henry! And it's not too hard a thing to do either, or the Lord wouldn't ask you to do it."

And that was the ultimatum Henry took with him to bed that night. There was no other way he could ever feel like singing *"Makes me love everybody."*

Henry was up before anybody that morning. He was up with the dawn. And head down, his spirit in his shoes, he dragged along the lane leading back through the woodlot to the McGuigan farm. He could just manage to keep going. The Lord was urging him on to the victory, and the Devil was urging him to be human. And once he had reached the woodlot, the Lord and the Devil reached a state of equilibrium within his soul and Henry stopped.

"I'm *not* going up to Tim's house with this ax! And I'm not going to make an apology and go through all that bawling around! I found the ax sticking on a stump right here in the bush and that's where I'm going to leave it!"

So he changed direction left and searched out the identical stump from which he had taken the ax in self-payment for the stolen crosscut. But suddenly he came to a startled halt, his attention attracted to a moving figure to one side of him. The morning was still full of foggy shadows, and he hadn't seen Tim until then. Nor did Tim see him. They both recognized each other at the same time. It was Henry who got angry first.

"You weasel!" he shouted. "What are you doing on our property? What is it you're aiming to swipe this time?"

Tim was very meek about it. "I just brought back a crosscut I stole from you a while back," he said quietly and looking awkwardly at his feet. "I—I got religion last night at the camp meeting. Last night after you went home . . . and you see I sort of had to make things right. You know how it goes."

It was Henry's turn to look at his feet and to talk quietly. "Yes," he said after a while, "I know how it goes, Tim. I'm here to put back your ax."

And half an hour later Henry came swinging and bouncing back down the lane from the woodlot, and at the top of his voice, singing until the melody rang like a bell across the morning meadows, *Makes me love everybody!*

How could anyone ever doubt, he wondered.

Chapter 4

THOSE WHO belonged to the proper churches in the town were seldom influenced by the camp meetings in their vicinity; they were apt to smile wisely when they heard of some unlikely person making a decision to change his ways. They guessed that such a conversion wasn't likely to be permanent. Not that they were against an occasional revival meeting so long as it was kept in good taste.

And when the news came back to Arthur that one of Bill Green's sons had got religion, the boys in the taverns also were certain that no permanent damage had been done, and others were equally sure that the decision couldn't last long.

The Greens, after all, were just about the most uninhibited family around. Bill and Mary Ann had brought ten boys into their small house in Arthur, and the incessant competition of their growing up had made battlers of all of them.

"Goodhearted blighters," you would have been told then, "and the hardest-working lads you ever did see. They're honest too, but just mind that you don't tangle tempers with them!"

So it provoked many a jest now to see one of the Green boys caught up by these curious glory people of Pepabun. Give the lad time, they said. Time would heal almost anything.

But they were wrong about Henry. Six years went by, and of the dozens who had taken their vows with him that July, so few remained now that the little church itself often threatened to give up the struggle and close its doors. But Henry Green still held calmly to his faith and his promise.

"He must of always been quieter than the others, don't you think?" the boys began to say now. "Sure now, it couldn't of been just religion that makes him so different than the rest!"

They thought perhaps that Henry was even too pious to love like a normal man. He had never gone out with anyone in his whole life but old Dave Blair's daughter, had he? And he didn't seem to be getting anywhere fast with her either. All he was interested in so far as the neighbors could see was that funny little church out in Luther, the twenty acres he had bought now next to the old Noble place, his carpentering and those squalling bagpipes he had adopted a couple of years ago. A strange kind of man, really!

What no one could know in this summer of 1910 was that Henry Green had quietly decided that he was ready to get married and that he intended to have Jean Blair whether her father gave his permission or not.

It was a September evening when he asked her. The

fields were brightly shaven, the down of recent threshings still clung to the leeward side of the barns and the orchards were red and fragrant. Henry was out on the bluff this evening with his bagpipes, and he was so brimming with emotion that he couldn't be still, stirred so deeply that he wanted to play the bagpipes all the time. But that love which is the most stirring is also the love of uncertainty and tonight the music faltered. First it was joyous and strong, and then it faded into longing, anxiety, even foreboding.

Things had been happening with dramatic swiftness of late, and last night for a second time Henry had asked Jean to marry him at once. "We could fix up the shack of mine, Jean," he explained. "It wouldn't be so bad for a year or so till I could build us something better. We wouldn't be far from your father; and if he wants to swallow his pride and make up I wouldn't be putting anything in his way."

He saw the threat of a tear come into her eye. He felt mean and put his arm about her, but he said nothing.

"Give me till tomorrow," she had asked. "I'll see you here on the rock at sundown tomorrow. Tonight I'll make up my mind."

"Tomorrow, it is then," he had said.

Now, coming along the concession that led into the dying sun, her shadow slim in the goldenrod, he could see her walking toward him. He didn't go to meet her tonight. No use making the woman think he was chasing her. He sat down on the rock and fingered the drones of his instrument, but his eyes never left her. Heavens to Betsy, but she was beautiful tonight! Her hair was whipping out behind her and she carried herself like a queen, and she was smiling. If Henry hadn't known her smile so well, his heart might have stopped in mid-beat for joy. But that smile wasn't quite natural. It was the smile of effort.

He kissed her gently and then held her at arm's length. After a while he said quietly, "So it's no again, Jeannie!"

"If we could only wait but a little while, Henry! Till spring. Or maybe even just three or four months . . . it would be so much better. . . . And time means so very little to people who love, dear."

"It's your father who says no then?"

"It's like I told you last night, Henry. Father's not well these days and he needs me to go south with him and see that he gets settled all right. Then maybe I can come back to you. . . . He's been a good father to me, Henry, and I won't always have him, you know."

Only last night she had told him the news. Her father had sold his farm and he was going to the city. The doctor had told him that his asthma was getting worse and that the farm was no place for a worn old man. But Henry was suspicious. The doctor had given that advice to Dave years ago, and Dave had always had the money to go had he wanted.

"The old man has tried everything else to get her away from me and it wouldn't work, so now he plays sick!" Henry thought fiercely. "All that's wrong is that I'm just not good enough for his daughter! I'm just one of the Green boys!"

Well, he had tried to make peace with Dave often enough and he had always failed. The break was inevitable. Might as well have it now. Dave was the only obstacle. Jean was quite content to set up housekeeping in his little story-and-a-half shack for a year or two until he could get her something better. Love could laugh at a little hardship. And besides, wasn't he doing more carpentering now than ever? It was Dave alone who stood between them now, and he would object as long as he lived.

"So we mark time waiting for the old man to die?" He knew his words would cut but he was getting angry in spite of himself.

She backed out of his reach and stooped for a head of clover. Her voice was gentle, as if she spoke to herself. "It's too bad that you and father must go on like this. You're both such good men really!"

"Is it my fault he hates me? Jean, you don't need to try to be polite to my feelings. It's nice of you to say that your father wants to have you with him because he's sick and he needs you. But you know the real reason why he's going to leave the farm now, don't you? He just doesn't think I'm any good and he'll do anything to get you out of my reach!"

"I think he's really sick, Henry. If I didn't, I'd marry you tomorrow. But he's sick."

Henry said, "I don't think he's any sicker now than he ever was. Maybe he wants breeding and background for his daughter. Maybe he even thinks I'm out to marry his money." He reached out and took her by the shoulder. His grip was surprisingly hard. "Yes, I'll bet that's it! He thinks I want to marry his money! Sure that's it!"

Her voice was still soft. "Henry," she said, "I have no more control over my father's faults than you had over your father's. But, Henry, no matter what he or anyone else thinks, I believe in you, and I'll come back just as soon as I can be sure Father is settled all right." She came close again and the fresh pink lips were very near and very sweet. But Henry turned away. He picked up his bagpipes to go home.

She ran after him and her tears came. "But I love you, Henry!"

His voice was gentle as always, but he couldn't keep the hurt from his words. "And how can a woman say she loves a man when she chooses another that hates him?"

Her tears came faster. Her words were smothered in weeping. "He's my father, Henry!"

"So long, Jean, and may your father find you a man with breeding and background when you get down there in the States!"

She didn't follow any more and Henry didn't look back. But long after she had gone back the way she had come and long after the rest of the farms up the concession had blinked off into slumber, Henry was striding slowly back and forth through the wet goldenrod, his pipes crying softly into the night, and his conscience accusing him as cruelly almost as it had done that time at the camp meeting.

A week later a livery rig drove into the lane. Henry resolved not to go out to meet it because the driver was a man who had obviously come up from the city, and whatever their business, Henry distrusted city slickers. But the driver didn't need to be met. He bounced out of the rig, bounced up to the back door and bounced his fist on the screen as if he were quite the busiest man on earth.

"My name's Singer," he announced. "I'm a real estate agent from Guelph, and I've just been looking at a little house the other side of Stumptown you built this summ for the miller. We'd like to know if you could find time t build another."

"Might. If I got my price."

"What would your price be for a house exactly the same as that one?"

"Same materials?"

"Same materials all the way through. No changes of any kind."

"How far would I have to drive to get this job?"

"Right next door as a matter of fact. A retired farmer has bought five acres of the old Noble farm from us and we've got to put a house on it for him. Now how much?"

Henry pondered. This man was trying to rush him and he didn't like to be rushed. Still, those who demand speed generally don't pause to quibble over cost, so Henry struck a figure.

"I took that last for twenty-two hundred dollars," he said, "but I was too low. I'll have to pay my help more this time and shingles have gone up too. I couldn't do it a chip less than twenty-seven hundred."

"When can you start?"

Henry was somewhat disturbed by so abrupt a surrender. On the one hand he accused himself for not asking a higher figure, and on the other hand his conscience smote him a little for asking so much. He had made a nice little pocketful on that last job, and even if shingles were dearer now, siding was down and in the end he could build just as cheaply. That extra five hundred dollars was pure gold.

He said, "I can start tomorrow. I'm all done harvest."

"Good. Now let's hop in my rig and go downtown. We'll get all arrangements signed off legally right this morning." And bounce, bounce, bounce, the real estate man was slapping his horse through the gate again.

That evening Henry went to the lumberyard to place his first order. Old Pete, the proprietor, met him with a smile. "Been expecting you," he said.

Henry pulled out his slip.

"Hear you've signed to build a house for old man Blair," said old Pete.

Henry looked up with a jerk. "What did you say?"

"You're building on the old Noble place, aren't you?"

"Yes," Henry replied calmly, "but I'm building for a real estate firm down in Guelph and nobody else."

"Maybe you didn't know that your friend Dave Blair bought the Noble farm the other day?"

Henry was as confused as he was angry. "But just three days ago old man Blair went to the city! So why should he be doing a thing like that?" he wanted to know.

"To make money maybe. With a house on that place it should bring a good price. Ought to make a very nice small holding for someone with a bit of money."

Henry felt cold purple creeping into his gills. "Pete," he said trying to contain himself, "are you kidding me?"

"You have only to inquire at the registry office to find out."

"And why didn't that real estate fellow tell me Dave Blair bought that place?"

Old Pete smiled. "Would you have signed a contract to build if you'd knowed Dave Blair was your boss?"

So that was it! Dave was still after money! He had seen a chance to dabble in real estate and make it pay. But he needed a job done and there was only one man around to do it—Henry Green! Not good enough for his daughter, mind you, but the one man who could do a job like this and at the right price! . . . Cute . . . cute as a fox! . . .

Henry said, "I'll not build the place. I'll be hanged if I will!"

"You'd be hanged then, Henry. You signed a contract, didn't you? And mind, you can be sure that when old Dave arranged it, he didn't leave any loopholes."

Henry said that he would have to go home and think awhile. But Pete had other ideas. "Come into the office where no one can hear us," he said. "There's something I want to tell you."

They went into the office. Old Pete did the talking. "It's like this. I've just found out that Dave and the girl are leaving for Florida next week. Doc suggested it and I guess the old boy figures he can afford a month or two with what he'll rake in from this deal. Now that means he won't be driving up here every week to watch you while you're building. . . . See what I mean?"

Said Henry, "Right now I can't see anything but red."

Pete slapped him on the chest, old-pal fashion. "Look, Henry, you signed to use the same materials this time as in that last place, am I right? Then what in the world is to prevent you from using some cheaper stuff instead of putting in the best like that other house? My yard's half full of seconds I'm trying to get rid of. I've got scantling and siding I can sell you a full ten dollars less a thousand, for instance. You're going to cover it with asphalt shingles anyhow."

"No," Henry replied quietly, "I've never cheated on a job yet and I don't aim to start now."

Old Pete threw up his hands. "Of course it's none of my business," he said. "Let him play you for a sucker if you want. But I know if it was me—well now, Henry, let's look at it this way. You've been double-crossed. Dirty double-crossed. Would it be wrong to double-cross back? I ask you—"

The idea didn't sound quite so bad when you looked at it that way, and then when Pete got down to figuring and showed him how many little ways there could be to save . . . well, first of all Pete had that batch of basement block. They looked just like any good cement block, but they had been made with too much dead sand in the mix and they wouldn't stand up. Crumbly. He could save a third, Pete said, and who was going to check twice on a basement anyhow? Then he had a lot of sill made out of homecut box elder. Looked exactly like pine and it might be years before it started warping. Well, months anyhow. He could get *them* for a third. Anyway couldn't he use poplar for studding? Cost a lot less than the hemlock he had put in that other place. He had wallboard same thickness exactly as in the last job that he could sell for half. Of course it would buckle with the damp after a while, but then who could blame Henry for that? And Pete could save him money on plumbing too. Who was going to rip up a sewage pipe to see if it were new or not? Then to get back to that siding . . .

And while Henry stood there, the Devil came and sat on his shoulder and put his arm around his neck and held his ear open, the Devil he thought he had shaken off once and for all in the grove at Pepabun. The Devil was very reasonable, very persuasive. "The old man's got it coming to him," he told Henry. "First he robs you of love and then he laughs at you with a trick. And suppose you should build true to your contract, be absolutely honest—would you get any credit for it? Has the old man ever given you any credit for the way you have tried all these months to outlive his bad opinion of you?"

And then when Henry picked up the sheet where old Pete had figured, the Devil whispered, "You could save at least four hundred dollars and the house would look exactly like the one you built before."

"I'll take till morning to think this over," Henry told Pete.

And because his heart was in the torment of temptation and writhing in the quest of decision, Henry took up his bagpipes that night. He began his march when the sun was below the goldenrod, level with the shadows. He was piping when the last red in the west had burned black and the moon warmed from chilly white to a gold that winked in the dew. And still he couldn't decide.

It was about ten-thirty when Jock MacPherson, the peddler, came up on his bicycle. Honest Jock, the women called him for he was an exceptionally reliable man. "Just getting back from a trip up Kenilworth way," he explained. "And I couldn't help but hear the pipes. It sort of does something to a Scot, ye know, coming up out of a September meadow on a night like this. Would ye mind playing me 'The Road to the Isles,' Henry, and then I'll promise ye I'll be off home."

So Henry played "Road to the Isles."

The peddler, true to his promise, threw his leg over his bicycle and pointed his headlamp homeward. "I surely thank ye," he said. "Man, but I love to hear a man play the pipes. Back by Edinburgh my father used to tell me that it was a *good* man who played the pipes—a man of integrity. A bad man couldn't."

Henry thought, "He doesn't know how near I am to proving his old man a fool." Out loud he said, "Now *that* I find interesting, Jock. Your father had his reasons no doubt?"

"Oh, something about the song of the pipes being the music of the soul, you know, and if there be no soul there can be neither music nor good works. Understand? Just a whimsey, I'll grant ye, but I'll always think of my father saying that when I hear the blast of the drones. Good night, Henry!"

Long after the peddler had wobbled off down the road, Henry sat steeped in thought, his pipes dangling lifeless at his side. So what was a man who played the pipes? A man of integrity. A man with a soul. A man given to good works. Well, suppose it was just a whimsey of some unknown cotter back by Edinburgh. It was a wholesome whimsey, and up till this moment Henry had done a pretty fair job of being that sort of a man. Why change it all for a sum of money now, even for four hundred dollars? What would he think of himself ever after?

Well, it was no sin to be tempted, he had often heard Harry Nelson say. And sometimes temptation was rather delightful.

Henry thought over the items on old Pete's sheet again. But this time the Devil had been ordered off his shoulder. Henry wondered now what on earth could ever have made him consider such a proposition. And then he began thinking of Jeannie, the way she had pleaded with him, her arms about his neck, her tears. And somehow he could no longer feel spite or hardness.

He jumped to his feet, swung his pipes over his shoulder with a mighty sweep, broke into one loud full joyous victorious verse of "Campbells Are Coming" and went home to bed.

In the morning he placed his order with old Pete. "I

know the old buzzard doesn't deserve it and he won't give me any credit for being honest when I could have been crooked, but I'm going to build that house just like I said I would," he announced. "I'd sooner be able to live with myself in peace than to have four hundred dollars in the bank and know I'd built a house that might fall in with the first high wind. Let's get to work, Pete!"

So Henry built the house. All that autumn he planned and pounded. Just like Pete had prophesied, Dave Blair never came near to inspect the building, and sometimes when the day had been unduly hard and Pete's laugh had a hint to it, Henry almost wished he had listened to the voice on his shoulder that day. But those were but passing fancies. At home after the sweat of the long day and when he was alone with his dog and his pipes, he was glad.

And little by little the house took shape, and finally one day when the corn rattled hard and lifeless in the stooks and only the pumpkins showed color, when the last of the apples lay useless on the ground and the gray grass had flints of snow huddled about the roots, the house was done.

It was late when his helpers had drawn their last pay and were gone home. But Henry lingered. He didn't know it, but he was in love with the place. He went down cellar and with his hammer he struck one of the basement blocks. It rang with strength. Solid. Last a lifetime. He thought of the man in the parable who built his house on sinking sand. . . . He looked above him and hammered a chip off the studding. He put the clean sliver in his mouth and chewed it. It tasted good. Hemlock. Straight as a die and it would be as straight fifty years from now. He went upstairs. He lifted a window and smiled inside at the easy way it hefted. White pine. Flawless white pine. No sapwood to bind a couple months from now. He went to the top floor.

And when he did, he heard a rig drive up the laneway. He looked out the bedroom window. It was the real estate man again. The rig stopped, the man bounced out, bounced up the walk and bounced his fist on the screen door. Henry went downstairs gathering wrath as he went.

But at the screen door, the man from the city talked faster than Henry did. "You've got the house all done? Good. I have my client out in the buggy. I'd like to bring him in. Perhaps you've met him. Mr. Dave Blair."

"I know him," Henry said sucking in his stomach. No use exploding till he got his money anyhow, he thought. Then he'd let them have it.

"Mr. Blair will want to see the place first and then we can finish our business inside where we have the light. Okay?"

So old Dave hobbled in, his brows pinched together, his lips tight as a vise and his precious old legal papers gripped in gnarly hands. Henry thought, "Maybe Jean was right about his really being sick. . . . I wonder what he'll find wrong. Plenty, you may be sure!"

They went through the house, Dave Blair ahead, then the agent, then Henry. When Dave Blair looked at the floor, Henry looked at the ceiling. When Dave Blair looked at the ceiling, Henry looked at the floor. And only the agent talked. But finally the two men faced and their eyes held. Dave Blair said grudgingly, "Well, I guess it will do."

They went downstairs and when they got to the built-in cupboard, the old man's fingers ungnarled from his papers, and he smacked them flat on the sideboard. He peeled a check from the top of the sheaf and handed it to Henry. Henry looked at it carefully. Well, he couldn't complain about that.

Then Dave thrust out a second paper. "Here," he said, "this is yours too."

Henry looked at it incredulously.

The old man seemed impatient. He didn't relish explanations. He seemed almost angry. "Don't know what that daughter of mine ever saw in a pipe-tooting chippy like you, but she would have you. Here! Take it, man! It's the deed to this house! Take it, because it's all the dowry I've got any intentions of giving you!"

It was much too sudden. Henry said, "I can't take it, Mr. Blair. I won't."

"Then I'll give it to Jean. It's all the same. She'll take it. Can't have any daughter of mine living in a shack, you know!"

At the door he paused and Henry thought he saw a bit of a smile teasing at the old man's lips. Dave said, "All right, drat it, you two have finally got your way so you've got no more excuse for not being happy! Good-by!"

And when Henry came to life he cried, "Jeannie! Where are you, Jeannie?"

She was coming up the pathway, running, laughing, crying, acting in that pitiful way happy women always act when they're happiest. But this time Henry ran too. She melted into his arms and nestled the smooth warmth of her cheek against the hard of his own. His words stuck. "I should of shaved this morning," he said at last.

He hugged her tighter and looked over at the house. His house. Their house. It was a wonderful feeling until he thought of that day at the lumberyard again—that day when the Devil had sat on his shoulder. Then for one awful moment he shuddered. But the next instant he felt marvelous again. He wanted to jump or holler or—well, he wished he had brought the bagpipes along.

But for once the pipes could wait till the morning.

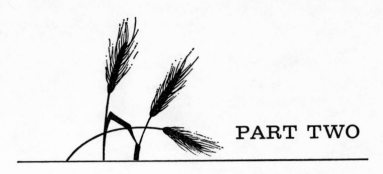

PART TWO

After We Came Along

Chapter 5

FROM OUR EARLIEST memories of him our father was always a quiet man, and undoubtedly his unusual tranquillity had come, at least in part, from the kind of labor which had been his. He had worked hard all of his young life, but that work had been the steady, unhurried kind of effort one expects from a man who never allows himself to become frantic with impossible ambition. Before we knew him, his years were spent in an unrelenting but confident struggle to cut himself a place in the sun: of tearing the tentacles of stubborn stumps from his own gray and stony piece of earth, and of slowly, slowly pushing back the line of forest until only the swamps were left. Later, in the days which we children remember so well, his task was an endless cycle of sowing and harvesting and of looking after his livestock.

And such a life has a tendency to develop thought rather than voice or language. The blue cold of winter winds, the whisper of pines and the association with contented animals are enough perhaps to make the philosopher of any man; but to our father this way of life also brought a unique kind of self-reliance. His family might *want* many things which he could never hope to give them, yet he knew that so far as their actual *needs* were concerned, there was little that could not be obtained through our own effort and patience.

The house which Father had been tempted to build to Satan's specifications once belonged to all of us now, and we kept it warm with our own woodfires. From our own fields came the wheat for our porridge and the oats and barley for our fowl and stock. From our own garden came the vegetables which filled our huge cellar bins—beets and carrots packed in sand, turnips, potatoes, pumpkins, winter radishes, parsnips, onions and popcorn ears hanging in bouquets from whitewashed timbers, cabbages hanging upside down where the dark was the thickest. In that cellar too were our fruit shelves, which, at the beginning of each winter, sagged beneath their plenty of canned preserves: blueberries from the marsh; raspberries from the knoll where the marsh lifted itself out of the muck to meet the woods; wild strawberries with the love of a little girl's fingers on every berry; wild plums and tame plums; cherries and chokecherries; apples, applesauce, apple butter and crabapple jelly; maple syrup still spiced with the tang of the wild spring nights in which it was brewed, and honey flavored with the recollection of our adventure in plundering it.

I wonder, now that the old farm has been surrendered to someone else, and all eight of us children are scattered over the country, what we remember most fondly about those days when we were all together in that house. The long

winter evenings perhaps, when we would sit around the
blazing stove listening to the storm tearing at the shingles
outside and spitting its frustrated anger down the chimney
at us while we read or played crokinole or clustered
around the oil lamps to do our homework? Listening to
father trying to play the pipes softly enough to keep
mother from flinching in protest?

Or perhaps some of us warm more quickly to think of
the animals which used to share that cozy security with us.
The dogs that could never be taught how to herd cattle,
for instance; and the cats that ran from rats, and all the
other strange creatures which were never of any use but to
cherish. The crickets we sneaked into the house each
harvest time and let loose behind the cookstove so we
could listen to their fiddling all winter long. The pan of
crayfish we brought from the creek and kept upstairs
beside the stovepipe which went through the boys' bedroom. The incubator in the parlor and the baby chicks
which were forever hopping over their box in the
kitchen.

Or, now that we have come to an age when it takes a
whole fleet of industries to pamper the appetite, maybe we
look back most longingly to the days when no one turned
up his nose at the smell of frying sauerkraut; when meat
came but once a day; and a cake at suppertime was so great
a luxury that there was only one carefully cut piece for
each of us.

What would I myself remember first should you ask me
to think of the old home? Ask that question sometime
when I'm hungry, or sometime when I wish I could be
hungry, and you'll have my answer in a second. I'll tell you
about our homemade bread.

Can you tell me why, if mother's bread had to go the

way of the horse and buggy and breast-fed babies, the bakers couldn't have given us something *nearly* as good?

Nor will it do to tell me that it is only the memories of childhood which have attached themselves to this product and made of it the perfect thing that I claim it to be. That there were memories connected with the making of bread back home, I would be the last to deny, for this was an institution which was almost as fascinating as it was important. First there was the buying of the yeast, which meant a trip down the road for one of us to the grocery with three cents sweating comfortably in the grip of the hand. Then the trip to the cellar for the carefully hoarded potato water, the cranking of the old sifter which was always out of round, and the waiting for the dough to rise. But most of all I remember that portion of the ceremony where the dough was to be punched. It was a job which was admirably suited for the energetic fists of children but the only trouble was that if a boy did not take enough time to first wash his hands as thoroughly as Mama had warned him to, the evidence would come off as soon as he tangled up with his work and the dough in the immediate vicinity of the unscoured fist would take on a tattletale gray that no amount of punching could quite sink out of sight.

And finally the great pans went to the oven. The oven of our old Happy Thought range had a crack which let in the light and smoke, and sometimes when we forgot to turn the loaves in time, one side would be as black as the oven itself.

But when the batch was right a loaf would come out looking for all the world like a big, plump, slightly sunbleached Buff Orpington hen, with the great thick ledges drooping from the rim marks as if her wings were let down to cluck.

And no matter how good it was, there was always enough of it!

To get back to the subject of bakers, how can these gentlemen try hard, as they say they do, and fail so miserably? Could it be the spray gun which puts that lovely old oak lacquer on the crust? Could it be the yeast they use? Are they absolutely certain that the brewers haven't used that yeast first before passing it on to them? Or is it simply that the modern baker has never devised a way of approximating such mysterious factors as those contributed by a cracked oven, or by motherly pride, or by a boy's grimy fists in the dough?

Someday perhaps, if I live long enough and my appetite keeps nagging me, I must write a story about that bread. Or at least a poem. But that is a topic which mustn't distract me now, because the intent of this book is to show how remarkably little concern our father had for bread of any kind—unless, of course, you refer to his faith as the Bread of Life.

I do not believe that Father was ever quite like the rest of the converts which Harry Nelson made at Pepabun. I can never recall him getting up in meeting to exhort or hearing him burst into the tearful prayers and hallelujahs. I think that there was something in the natural calm of his character which would have always prevented this. I doubt that he could ever have become a fanatic. Nevertheless his was an abiding faith, and one which outlived many another which seemed to have fallen from heaven with much more fire and glory.

To Father, God's reward was not always in direct proportion to the amount of honest effort expended, but the reasons for this seeming lack of Divine justice were merely among the many other mysteries which would have to be made clear on the other side. It wasn't for us to know such things now.

And whatever his momentary doubts may have been, he could never believe that there could be any excuse for changing the interpretation of Holy Writ to suit the whims of a modern age which was hell-bent and sick with worldliness. As for him and his house, they would serve the Lord!

Every night but Sunday, after the homework and the crokinole, and before we were bundled off up the dark stairs to our beds, there would be a reading from the Bible storybook, a hymn or two and then we would kneel beside our chair while Mother or Father offered a simple prayer.

How gloriously fortunate we were to be of the true faith! The Bible had said that "Strait is the gate, and narrow the way . . . and few there be that find it." We were of those few.

But like any other faith which is absolutely certain of its absolute righteousness, such a creed could be cruel and intolerable as often as it was simple and beautiful. And this book would never have been written if the original harsh fervor of our father's faith hadn't mellowed with time. And perhaps the earliest vivid memory I can recall of this mellowing is of the year that Father Kelly came into our lives.

It never occurred to our father in the early days of his faith that his attitude toward the Catholics of the section should have been one of tolerance rather than scorn. He, like most in the Protestant community, had long cherished a traditional distrust and scorn for his Irish neighbors.

Even those Protestants who never attended a church and who practiced no more religion than what they got from going to funerals or eating hot cross buns in Lent, were quite capable of practicing a righteous hate.

I recall that as schoolboys we used to excite ourselves by discussing some of the many tales we had heard about the "well-known fact" that the basements of many Roman Catholic churches were filled with guns and bombs, ready for the great day when the Pope would make his fatal bid for domination of the world. I remember too that if, on some day when we were unusually brave, we met a Catholic boy on the road, we were apt to yell "Dogan Dog!" at him. And if he could run fast enough, he would probably reply with a vicious "Protestant Pup!"

Chief defender of a militant Protestant heritage in our area was the Orange Lodge, a fearless and gloriously colorful organization which had been imported to Ontario from Northern Ireland. Each July on the Glorious Twelfth, the anniversary of the victory of William of Orange at the Battle of the Boyne and the end of the Catholic kings of Britain, the Lodge held a celebration which was generally even more exciting than that of Dominion Day. From miles around, farmers would flock into the village clad in white jackets trimmed with orange and purple. There would be the inevitable fife and drum bands, great tasseled banners, a resurrected King "Billy" on a white horse to lead a parade up Main Street, lacrosse and ball games and speeches filled with joyous brooding about the threat of unholy Papist ambition. And sometimes, if there were Catholics available and these were brave enough, there would be broken heads before the day was over.

We boys were generally even more Protestant than our elders on that day, and after buying a handful of orange and purple ribbons we would march up the road into the middle of the Irish section singing

> Teeter totter, holy water
> Sprinkle the Dogans every one,
> If this won't do we'll cut 'em in two
> And bury them under the Orange and Blue.

And as the dogs from the Catholic homes would come rushing out to bark at us, we would catch them, tie our brilliant ribbons to their collars and tails and stone them back up the lane. Sometimes we were met by a band of Irish lads who met our taunts with sticks, stones and bare fists. And I remember that on those rather numerous occasions when I had cause to shed blood, I did so with a certain thrill of holy zeal such as a Crusader might have had.

I don't recall that Father ever scolded me for such adventures. One expected a lad to be aware of his Protestantism. I do remember him scolding me once however for referring to the new priest in town as "Father " Kelly.

"Never mind that 'Father' stuff when you're talking about any priest!" he warned me. "He's not God, is he?"

But as God would have it, it was this same Father Kelly who first took some of the sternness from father's faith and broadened its horizons—Father Kelly and his blue rose. Because Father and the village priest, for all the awesome differences between them, had one thing in common: They both loved flowers.

Mother used to complain rather bitterly sometimes about the space that was given to flowers in our garden. "Upon my word, Henry!" she would say, "I just don't understand how a man can be so impractical! How much did you pay for those lily bulbs anyhow? And I still haven't got those gooseberry and currant bushes I asked for!"

Father would never hoe vegetables in the garden on a Sunday, but with flowers it was different. He seemed sure that there could be nothing sinful about tending a flower bed on the Sabbath.

The priest too had a lovely garden, and when father and I would drive by with grist or with a load of lumber from the mill, he would always slow the team as we came in sight of the priest's house.

"Not as good as mine though," he would say keeping his eyes on the flowers until we were long past the place. Yet I knew that he itched to stop and see that garden. And one day he did stop. "Lad!" he said to me excitedly, "doesn't that look like a blue rose to you?"

It did look like a blue rose.

Father climbed down from the wagon and began walking toward the white picket fence. And at that moment the priest straightened up and showed himself above the rows of shrubs and blooms. He smiled as if in welcome, but Father turned in embarrassment and remounted his wagon without a word.

It was the following Sunday afternoon, I think, when the priest drove his spanking buggy up our lane, knocked at our back door and asked if our dad might be in.

"I hope I'm not disturbing your Sabbath, Mr. Green," he said when Father showed himself, "but I just can't keep my eyes off those big white lilies you've got out front. Would they be Creelmans by any chance?"

Father hid his uneasiness and answered that they were Creelmans all right. And with some doubt about the rightness of what he was doing, he led the way around the side of the house to his beloved flowers.

" 'Consider the lilies of the field,' " Father Kelly recited softly as they came to the flowers which had so fascinated him, " 'how they toil not, neither do they spin; yet I say unto you that Solomon in all his glory was not arrayed as one of these.' "

Had it been anyone but a priest who had quoted that scripture, Father's heart would have gone out to him at once, but he must be on guard now. The Devil himself could quote scripture.

"I guess maybe I've sort of grew them too tall this year," Father said. "I put an awful lot of cow manure on them."

But when the priest took one of the gorgeous blooms in his hands and looked into it as if it held a soul in its depths, Father's reserve began to melt a little.

"A jewel!" the priest exclaimed quietly. "Ah, but it's better than a jewel! Back in Ireland, my sainted grand-mother had a definition all her own for flowers," he said. "She insisted that they were God's thoughts."

Father seemed to toss his nagging conscience behind him after that and he eagerly showed the priest every flower and shrub in the garden. And when Father Kelly protested that he really must go now, I was secretly scuttled off into the house to make sure that Mother would have a pot of tea and a pie ready. "Mind that she uses the black tea," Father warned me. "The Irish like their tea strong."

But it wasn't until many weeks and many teapots later that Father finally mustered the courage to ask the terribly urgent question which had never been out of his mind. "Kelly," he began the evening that the priest came up with a slip from his Blue Rambler rose, "you'll pardon me for being so frank, but for the life of me I can't understand how a man as decent as you, and as smart, can be a Catholic!"

I remember that they were sitting out on the back porch that night and that the priest laughed so hard at Father's seriousness that the dog jumped up and barked at him. Then the priest too became serious.

"Yes, it is strange, isn't it?" he said. "Strange how two men equally conscientious, equally intelligent and equally prayerful can both set out to find the truth and yet can come to conclusions that are as different as—well, as St. Francis of Assisi and your friend Harry Nelson. I—I just haven't got the answer to that one, Henry. I guess it's just one more of those mysteries that won't be unraveled till we make the yon side of the gates. . . . On the other hand, I suppose maybe a man's belief sort of grows out of what was planted in him in the beginning. Maybe you can't expect County Cork to grow a Protestant any more than you can expect that Blue Rambler there to sprout lilies. . . ."

Long after we boys were snug in the valleys of our straw ticks that night, bits of the talk on the back porch kept drifting up to us. But we had to strain our ears to listen, and after a while we had to give up trying to make proper sense out of it. There didn't seem to be enough argument or passion in either voice to lift it all the way to our bedroom windows.

A couple of weeks later it was the Glorious Twelfth again and Father told us that this year he didn't think he'd bother to march in the parade. "And you," he said turning sharply in my direction, "I want you to leave off this here catching Catholic dogs and sending them down the road with their tails full of firecrackers! Mind what I say now!"

And one day that next September when I told my father

that the priest was organizing juvenile lacrosse downtown and that I wanted to try to make the team, he offered no objection at all.

"I guess you'll not kill yourselves too often with Father Kelly keeping an eye on you," he said. Meaning that I could say "Father" Kelly too now if I wanted.

Chapter 6

I KNEW IT would be a rough ride to town that Saturday morning, because the ruts were set like cement with a frost that September should have been ashamed of, and there was no more give to our grain wagon than there was to the ruts. But I was nine then and thought myself fully come to a time when it behooved me to put away childish things and act like a man. So what were a few bumps and a pair of cold feet? And how old did my protesting mother think I was now, anyhow?

I didn't tell Mother, of course, the real, pressing reason why I had to take that trip with my father that morning, for I knew better. Even after I was finally up on the wagon alone with him, it took all of two miles before I finally got up the courage. "Dad," I said, "us guys in the lacrosse team are going to play the gang in Kenilworth next Friday after four. Father Kelly is taking us up."

"Uh huh," my father said, coming down out of his worries to listen. "That's nice. Good game, lacrosse."

I knew he would like that part of it, for a few years back my father had been a great lacrosse man himself. "I'm going to play goal for our side," I hurried on. "I've got to have a goal stick."

My father began to rub one finger beneath his nose and he looked out across the frosted fields.

"I've *got* to have a goal stick!" I said, feeling my throat beginning to clog up on me. "Daddy, couldn't we—couldn't you lend me three dollars out of this load of grain? I could pay you back sometime!"

My father turned his short body half around and nodded at the load of sacked grain. "Today is tax day," he said quietly. "And I'm afraid what's left over won't even buy what groceries your mother needs."

I knew all that, because when Mother had made out the list she had spent a lot of time juggling the items around until they were finally down in the order of their importance. But in all my life I had never wanted anything so desperately as I wanted this goal stick! I *needed* it! The whole team was depending on me.

I am not quite sure now whether the sharpness of my disappointment set me to crying, or whether my father just noticed that I was on the verge of it. All I remember is that he began twisting his forehead in his hand. And then he said, "Well, give me a little time, lad. Give me time to think it over. Something might turn up, you know."

The something turned up with such suddenness that it seemed like nothing less than the direct intervention of God Himself. It came out of the way we weighed in our load at the grain elevator. First you drove onto the scales, team, wagon and all; and old Seth Cambridge, who owned the place, went inside the little cubicle at the side of the platform to take the reading. Then you drove forward to the unloading ramp, left your grain there and backed your team and wagon onto the scales again to have their combined weight subtracted from the first reading.

I knew old Seth and I knew his son Mart, and I had never liked either of them. The reason I didn't like Seth was my father's reason, I guess, because Dad had been pretty sure that Seth had short-changed him more than once. And besides that, he was too surly for any good use. I don't quite remember now why I had never liked Mart, but it might have been merely because he was a son of his dad, or more illogically still, because he was one of the town "slickers" who were always carrying on undeclared warfare on those of us who came from the farm.

Whatever it was, I felt very jubilant when I learned of the trick which had been played on the Cambridge firm. It was Sandy MacDonald, who stood two teams ahead of us in the line, who played the trick first. His lad had ridden to town that morning the same as I had, and because it was so cold waiting, he had lain down in the wagon box beside the sacks of oats. And when weighing time came, he hadn't bothered to get out with his father.

But when it came time to drive ahead to unload, my schoolmate got out of the wagon and he stayed out.

His father was still laughing about the mistake when he was coming away from the mill with his check in his hand. "Well, well, well, Bud!" I heard him say. "You're worth something after all! You're worth exactly the same price as oats this morning! Three cents a pound!"

Never in my life had I worked out a multiplication so fast. I weighed 82 pounds that year. Three times 82 was . . . $2.46. The lacrosse stick which I had to have—the one which was right now waiting patiently for me in Gillen's hardware—cost three dollars, but it wouldn't be hard to find that last half dollar.

"Dad!" I said, "I'm going to do it too!"

Eagerly, I watched my father's stolid, wind-whipped face, saw him rub the side of his rough finger under his nose again. "Don't just know about that," he said quietly. "Not that I'm exactly in love with old Seth but—"

Almost frantically, I began to argue. I reminded my father of the times when Seth had cheated *us*. I reminded him of the hundred pounds of timothy seed which we had weighed on two different scales just to make sure that it was a hundred, and still Seth had declared that there was only 96 pounds of it. And then there had been the time when Dad had come home to find that eight of his best canvas grain sacks hadn't been returned to the wagon after the oats had been dumped out of them.

I argued till the pain of my wanting swelled my throat shut, and finally my father said, "Well, it *does* seem that we'll never get a chance like this again to pay that old sucker back. Only—"

He never finished. I didn't want him to finish. Old Seth was impatiently beckoning us onto the scales, and the minute he turned his back I dove into the back of the wagon and buried myself deep in the sacks. We pulled to a stop on the scales and I held my breath as my father got out for the weighing. The wait was almost more than I could stand.

And then suddenly it was all over and we were off the scales and drawing abreast of the unloading platform. Cautiously, I cocked an eye over the tailboard, and then slid out to the ground. How could it have been so easy, I wondered. But I kept my thoughts to myself until my father had thrown the last sack over the side of the wagon and emptied it into Seth's hopper. Then, smiling with relief and victory, I sidled up to my father and whispered, "How much am I worth a pound, Dad?"

My father undid the reins from the ring at the side of the platform, and without getting into it, prepared to back the wagon onto the scales again. "Get in," he told me.

He had to tell me twice because the first time, I couldn't believe that he would be so heartless. "I said to get in," he said. "Not that I don't see your point, but there's some things I just don't do." And he took hold of the seat of my pants and hoisted me back into the wagon. I was surprised that he would be so firm.

Seth looked at me in astonishment when the wagon backed onto the scales, and my father explained. "He was in when you weighed it first," he said. "And I'm not selling him, I guess. Not for three cents a pound."

I didn't say a word about the lacrosse stick until we were out of the millyard and heading down the village street. And then my voice came back to me in a rush of tears and temper. "I could have had my stick easy as pie!" I cried. "But you wouldn't let me! You don't *want* me to have a stick, I guess!"

My father looked straight ahead for a long time, and then he began to rub the wrinkles out of his forehead again. "If you got the stick that way," he said quietly, "I don't think it would ever play right. . . . And anyhow, I've been thinking maybe I could make a stick for you."

"You're going to *make* one!" I said derisively. "Great-looking stick you could make!"

But he did make one. He went out into the woods almost as soon as we got home that day, and after he had searched for two hours or more, he came back with an ash limb. He spent all that night and most of the next, steaming and whittling and shaping, and then when he had the wood finished to his liking, he cut up an old harness and set to work to gut it.

But it was a rather clumsy-looking affair in spite of all his skill and effort, and my father grudgingly admitted it. "It'll last you the first game anyhow," he said, "and maybe after that we'll find a way to get the other one. Here, you tape it yourself."

I hefted it and ran my fingers over the crook where the ash was already beginning to splinter. I said nothing one way or the other.

"It'll do better for you than the other one would of anyhow," Father said, turning away. "And that's all I can do for you now."

The big game was played that next Friday night and the battle went on till the dark made it impossible for us to follow the ball any more. And after the game came the fight.

My mother gave a little scream when I first came through the door that night. "Your face!" she cried. "It's two sizes too big for you!"

Father said nothing but he went at once for the washbasin and warm soft water. "Now how in the world did that happen?" he asked when he had the worst of the carnage washed clear. "Looks to me like you were in a fight."

I didn't want to, but I had to tell him that he was right.

"I don't like fights in a game," he said. "Not in lacrosse anyhow. It's too easy to get hurt. Now what were you fighting about?"

I did my best not to tell him, but as soon as he saw that I was trying to hold something back he was all the more insistent. "There were some guys on the other team and they were teasing me about my stick!" I blurted out. I hadn't let a whimper out of me when Father was putting iodine on my cuts, but now I had to cry like a baby. "They said I must have an Indian for an old man!" I cried. "And they said it was against the rules to play with a stick like that!"

I knew it would hurt him. I knew it would hurt him far more than it did me, only he wouldn't show it, and I would have done anything if I could have kept my trouble to myself.

"Well," he said very quietly, and looking over to where the goal stick stood in the woodbox behind the stove, "it does look pretty homely, I guess. Maybe we can figure out some way to get you the right kind one of these days."

Which he did before I played another game. He got me the beautiful stick I had seen at the hardware, and when I first hefted it and tested the give of its pocket and smelled the new oil of its rawhide I was as happy as any Christmas. But later, when I found out how Father had found the money for this wonderful gift, I had to go up to my room until the swelling went out of my throat. Because Father had sold his bagpipes to get this for me.

"Well, I had to find a little extra money for other things too," he told me quietly when I scolded him for doing such a thing. "Taxes were awful high this year, it seems. It wasn't just on account of you wanting the lacrosse stick exactly."

But I knew that he was only trying to clear the air so I would go back to enjoying my stick again.

Chapter 7

THE OTHER DAY as I was blowing the dust from a half-forgotten section of my library, I unexpectedly came across the very first book which my father ever gave me. It is a battered little volume about the size of a postcard, commonly known as a bird guide, and the subtitle reads, *Land Birds East of the Rockies,* by Chester A. Reed, copyrighted 1909. Price $1.25. One bird to a page, each in full color and complete with details of its song, habitat, color, etc.

It is bound—or it was once—in limp brown linen, but over the years the cover has disappeared. And if you look too closely you will see that many of the tattered pages would have been lost too had they not been reinserted and made fast with carpenter's glue.

And as I sat down to thumb through those very familiar pages again and remembered how that book came to me, I began to wonder in a whimsical way why it is that children no longer know how to "stamp" robins.

In my own schooldays, the enchantment one placed

upon his life by "stamping" robins was quite as important a part of childhood lore as getting warts from a toad, or telling your fortune by skipping rope, or making it rain by stepping on a spider. And of course everyone knew how to perform the rite properly. When you saw your very first robin of spring, you made a fist of your left hand, licked the ball of your right thumb, pressed the wet thumb to your left fist and then struck both fists together. You repeated this magical process every time you saw another robin, and you kept it up until the country had so many robins in it that it was too big a chore to keep on stamping them.

There was apparently no specific reward for performing this unique ceremony—just general good luck. And the longer you kept on stamping your robins, the sooner your good luck would come.

Birds are apparently no longer so dear to the hearts of our youngsters, but that isn't so surprising perhaps because we who are old enough to know better have let the birds fade out of our lives too. And perhaps it was my conviction that this is the kind of loss which this hypertensed generation can least afford which set me thinking back as I did to the story of this tattered bird guide and that most unforgettable of all the Easters I have ever known—that Easter when birds seemed more important than all else in the world.

But before you can really understand how this could be, I suppose I should first tell you something about my father. For even in a day when a farmer was in much closer communion with nature than he can be now, my father had a most unusual love for birds. You will be more ready to believe that perhaps if I tell you that they even affected his plowing.

Forty years ago, when all the horsepower on the farm still belonged to the horses and a man did his plowing a furrow at a time, it was very important for that furrow to be very straight and even. Not that faultless furrows guaranteed any heavier oats, but the quality of a man's plowing was somehow regarded then as a sort of measure of his character.

So it was somewhat humiliating for us boys to learn one spring that our father's plowing was the reason for some laughter among our neighbors.

"Henry," the creamery man said one day, "what the sam hill is wrong with your plowin' lately? I swear it looks as if the sun had warped it!"

And someone else asked him one day why all the islands had been left stuck here and there all over the field. Were those the places that were too tough to turn over?

Our father, being a man who never argued, merely smiled and seemed to enjoy the jest as much as anyone else. Why in the world, we boys asked one another, wouldn't he explain? To insinuate that our dad was a sloppy plowman was worse than nonsense. He was one of the best in the county. And if you didn't believe it, all you had to do was to look at the plowing which he did in the fall. No islands in that, and every furrow of it as straight as a die. It was only in the spring that Dad's plowing was crooked and crazy and we knew why.

Every spring, when the killdeers came north again, dozens of them would make their threadbare nests in the tough clay of my father's fields. Who knows? Maybe the word had been passed among them that they had been safe here. Then when it came plowing time, and the horses came dangerously near to them, the killdeer, in an attempt to lure the intruder away from its nest, would flutter out in front of the team, dragging itself along the ground as if wounded, and filling the whole landscape with its plaintive, mercy-begging calls.

And when that happened our father would stop the team, find the endangered nest, drive a stake in the ground beside it to mark its position and then circle his plow around it.

As long as we could remember, he had been doing that. He did it so often in fact that before a spring plowing was half done, the team would stop of its own accord every time a killdeer fluttered out in front of them and set up its wailing.

To get back now to the bird guide, it was given to me on my thirteenth birthday. Underneath my porridge bowl it was that morning, its breathtaking beauty protected by a suitable box as if it were a jewel of some sort. And even today when I think of the sacrifice which bought it, its colors are still tear-bright and lovely.

I say that it was a birthday present, but it was really something more than that. It so happened that year that my birthday came very near to Easter, and I am sure that this wonderful little book was something in the nature of a surprise Easter present for all of us. After all, on a farm such as ours, with only forty acres to feed all ten of us, a mere birthday was rarely an excuse for a present—not the kind which cost money anyhow.

I'll always remember how Father found the money for that book. It was Mother who gave the secret away. "Why, Henry!" she said, a little shocked by this extravagance. "Where did you get that dollar and a quarter to spend like that?"

Then she remembered where. Dad had been cutting birch and poplar in the swamp that year, and he had been complaining of chilblains. He needed wool socks and she had given him enough money for two pairs. He never bought them.

"Oh well," Father said defensively, "the cold weather must be over now. The birds are coming back. . . . But mind that you take good care of the book, lad."

I suppose that if one were wise enough now to analyze motives, he could be cynical and say that the giving of this memorable little book was basically selfish. After all, it was something Dad wanted desperately for himself. But we weren't clever enough to worry about that. This was a gift for all of us. Let a bird which looked the least bit un-familiar settle down long enough for any of us to see him, and immediately out would come the bird guide. And before the book was tucked away in its jewel case again, every one of us would know the name of that bird, where he came from, how long he was likely to stay and what he did for a living.

As might be expected, Father learned more than the rest of us. He found out for instance that the early bird he had always called a "cutthroat" was really the horned lark; that the gorgeous red birds which sometimes stopped off to inspect our balsams weren't wheatears as he had always claimed, but cardinals; and his beloved killdeer wasn't even in the book because the man who had written it insisted that the killdeer was a plover and hence not rightly a land bird at all.

"Funny thing but the killdeers don't seem to know they're water birds either," Dad said once. "Anyhow they sure seem to like our land. . . . Here, lad, put the book away again. Better patch up the corners of that box, hadn't you?"

Now I know that we still have bird watchers with us,

and there is surely no finer hobby anywhere. But however pleasant the pastime of bird watching may be in this age of scientifically insulated and automatically heated winters, I know that it can never hold quite the same thrill that it did forty years ago when I was a boy. Then, as defense against the relentless fury of the elements, we had only the woodpile, the kettle singing on the stove and our itchy all-wool "combinations." For the most part, winter was something one was expected to endure, nor murmur not.

So the coming of those first brave birds back from the south was something far more than an interesting lesson in nature study. It was a sort of proof—divine proof, perhaps —that silence and cold and lifelessness do not mean death after all; that the soul of earth was only sleeping; and that the idea of resurrection was not just a nebulous story of hopeful piety which one found in the New Testament, but a glorious, vibrant, throbbing miracle which one could witness for himself every spring. And the return of the birds brought that miracle as near to us as the nearest tree, or even to the windowsill.

For my God-fearing father I suspect that there was an element of contemplative devotion in his bird watching— the kind of contemplation and devotion which this age of insatiable science has all but lost even though it may need it much more than he did.

If you think that I have become much too sermonish about this, you will still agree with me that it's a great shame to learn that our children no longer know how to "stamp" robins.

Surely it's a sad day indeed if they are learning nothing more than what the schools are giving them now.

Chapter 8

MY FATHER WAS too shy a man to attempt any tune he thought might be heard, and yet I can recall his singing now as if I had heard it but yesterday morning. And the song which always comes first to mind is an old favorite which he must have learned at one of the Pepabun camp meetings:

> By and by, when the morning comes
> All the saints of God will gather home;
> We will tell the story how we overcome,
> And we'll understand it better by and by.

Early, while we children were still snug and lazy in our straw ticks, we would hear him singing out this triumph all the way down the lane, beating out the lively lilt of it with a gad on the side of his boot. We would hear him singing all the way down to the pasture gate, where the cattle too would hear him and come lowing out of the shining mists to meet him.

I have already protested that Father was no zealot. Like most men whose faith is really profound, he lived quietly with his religion. And as I look back now at the days when we shared the warmth of his house, I cannot help but marvel that he could have achieved so sure a belief in a Creator who was all good and always concerned, when his life had so much of struggle and heartbreak in it.

Our soil was heavy and sour, and there were but forty acres of it to sustain eight children. Father himself had been one of a pioneer family of eleven. He had but three years of schooling.

Yet even in the grim years of the great depression, I can never remember him voicing the slightest doubt of the ultimate goodness of the Master Plan.

"Oh well, it will all work out!" he would say.

There were always those of his friends who refused to believe that such a steadfast faith could be the result of anything so impulsive as a camp-meeting conversion. But certainly no one could say that Father's religion was part of his inheritance. My grandfather, Bill Green, had died shortly after Father married—died as dramatically as he lived, beneath a falling tree. And while his jests about his son's saintliness were kindly, he never once was anything but the bitter skeptic who had once argued with Harry Nelson. And though Mary Ann, our tough little grandmother, never for one moment doubted the existence of the Almighty, she was quite outspoken in her conviction that He was too often not inclined to follow the law of love He had handed down for the guidance of mortals. And if she ever got within earshot of Him someday, she would sure have some pretty pointed questions to ask Him too!

"Well, Mother," Father would say after he had patiently listened to her sacrilegious accusations, "for now, I guess all we can have is faith. If it's proofs we want, well, I reckon it's just like that song I call the cows with in the morning. We just have to believe that we'll understand it better by and by!"

Yet my father's faith wasn't entirely based on the "evidence of things not seen." Sometimes, right here on this earthly side of Jordan, the proofs were so crystal clear to him that he couldn't for the life of him understand how anyone could ever doubt.

Our little friend Prunejuice was one of these.

We had come now to that period of our family history when we no longer went to the church at Pepabun every Sunday. The winters alone were reason enough why we could not make that eight-mile trip regularly, even after the wonderful day when we got our first Model T. But besides that, the mellowing which had begun with Father Kelly's blue rose had now brought our father to the point where he saw nothing wrong in having his family attend one of the more democratic churches in the village. I think he did this with some misgivings, however, for as soon as the mud and cold of spring had disappeared, we would drive out to be with the saints again. And always, always we attended the camp meeting. The brush arbor had given way to a huge tent now, but other than that the service could have changed but little.

And on the final Sunday morning of one of those meetings, when it was discovered that the treasury was dangerously low, we were all given the benefit of a special sermon on stewardship. The evangelist that year was a colorful old glory thumper who had come up from Kentucky for the week. He was a man who, to use the saints' own expression for him, was surely "on fire for God."

"Now see here, brethren!" he shouted, "it's a downright disgrace for us to be so hard up for money! The Lord is a good provider, isn't He? Well, what's wrong here then? Why are we scraping the bottom of the barrel like that widow in Zarepath? Well, I'll tell you why! Because we are just afraid to put our faith to work for us, that's why! Well, brethren, I'm here this morning to tell you we're going to change all that!"

Gradually he made the plan clear to us. The ushers would take no collection that morning. Instead, he had induced the board to withdraw most of the money which still remained in the bank and reduce it all to new dollar bills. These had now been divided into the four collection baskets, and the ushers, looking rather red and uncomfortable at this moment, were to pass those baskets through the congregation.

"Brethren!" cried the evangelist with a dramatic shake of his jowls, "these here ushers are not going to ask you for one cent when they wait on you this morning! This time they're asking you to *take* money! There's seven hundred dollars in those baskets right now: seven hundred dollars of the Lord's money. And all we're asking you to do is to take out what you figure would be a right share of this and invest it for the Lord. Most of you are farmers. Maybe you'll want to buy a baby pig with that money. Or maybe you'll put in a special planting of some kind. . . . I'm not going to advise you how to invest it, because the Lord will tell you that when you get around to asking Him. . . . All I'm asking is that whatever you do, you do it with enough faith to believe that the Lord will attend to His own. Then when next camp-meeting time rolls around and it's time to pass these here baskets out to you again, we're going to ask you to just give the Lord back His own money! . . ."

I can still recall the look of bewilderment which came over the faces of the congregation when the evangelist had explained the last detail. True, the idea was hardly original even then, but it was so new to the saints and so utterly daring that some of the older men began to whisper amongst themselves in alarm. Sure, here was a preacher full of the spirit and all that, but after all, he *was* an American. And these Americans had a weakness sometimes for being spectacular rather than sensible.

Father had his reservations too. "I'm not too sure just how stable that man is," he whispered to Mother. "Seems as though we're supposed to put God on trial!"

But in the end he took five fresh bills, same as most of the others did; and all the way home that afternoon he and Mother kept wondering how they should invest it.

"It's almost too late to do any planting with it," Father concluded. "And it's got to pay off by this time next year. So looks to me as if it will have to buy some sort of livestock."

In the end, they decided that the five dollars should buy a setting of hatching eggs. Chickens grew the quickest. And besides, there seemed less risk involved. A single fatality wasn't going to wipe out the whole project.

The only trouble was that Mother had chickens of her own—a lovely flock of White Wyandottes. "We'll have to buy some kind that's different now," she said. "Else we won't be able to keep track of them handy."

Father had several reasons for choosing Dark Brown Leghorns besides the fact that there could be no mistaking them with Mother's Wyandottes. Of all the advertisements in the farm paper, only the Dark Brown Leghorns were quoted at five dollars per setting. All the rest were much cheaper. So not only did such a choice make for easy bookkeeping, but it also meant that the Lord was getting the very best.

I am convinced that the other reason arose from the fact that in those impractical days there wasn't the same cold separation between poultry and poetry as there is now. No one made fun of a farmer for choosing a particular breed for its beauty of feathering as much as for its earning power.

Of all the fowl which ever strutted in the sun, the Dark Brown Leghorn is surely one of the most gorgeous; and I am certain that Father was thrilled with the prospects of having some of them soon in his own barnyard.

A setting—in case you're too absorbed in progress to know this—means fifteen eggs. We got sixteen for good measure. It was July now and Mother's henhouse had more than its quota of clucking hens. "Think we should risk all these eggs under one hen?" Father asked our mother. "Don't you reckon it would be less risk if we divided the lot and set two hens on them?"

So it was that two hens, each covering eight eggs, were given the divine mission of hatching out the Lord's eggs.

"Now then," Father said as he tacked some screening over the two nests to insure privacy, "you two old biddies just sit there and think about those eggs for twenty-one days and that's all we'll ask."

One of the hens, however, was not at all impressed by the sacredness of her job, and two days before her eggs were to have hatched, she forced her way out of her nest and wouldn't go back. And by the time we discovered her rebellion, her eggs were cold and lifeless.

The other clucker was faithful to the end, but for all her

trouble, only three chicks broke out of their shells on the twenty-first day.

Father moved the mother hen and her three fluff bits into an empty stall and gave her a supply of feed and water. "Sure couldn't have been much vitality to those eggs," he said shaking his head.

It was bad luck indeed, but the worst was yet to come. For no good reason that anyone could see, two of the chicks gave up the ghost that first day. And the one remaining was now so precious that father took it away from the hen and gave it a box behind the kitchen stove.

"Isn't it pretty?" one of my little sisters cried hugging it to her cheek. "And just the color of prune juice!"

"Well, Prunejuice," Father said taking the chick away from her, "you're sure going to have to lay one awful lot of eggs between now and next camp-meeting time, if you're ever going to pay the Lord back his five dollars!"

But a few weeks later, when fluff gave way to feathers and a little scarlet comb began to bud out, it was all too evident that Prunejuice would never lay any eggs at all. For Prunejuice had decided to become a rooster.

But almost from the start it was plain to see that Prunejuice wasn't likely to be any ordinary rooster. He grew like a weed and he was incredibly precocious. "No wonder the rest of those eggs was so weak," Father used to say. "This bird has it all!"

The affection which soon developed between the cocky young bird and the family was, of course, inevitable. While he was still a chick in the down stage, Prunejuice even went to bed with us, for Father kept him in a little box near the head of the bed with the lamp burning in it all night to keep him warm. And it was the maintenance of that lamp which necessitated the first entry in Prunejuice's expense account.

"Extra coal oil, 10¢," Father wrote on the back of the calendar.

It wasn't long, however, before Prunejuice had no need of further mothering, and when that day came, we tried leaving him in the henhouse with the other fowl. But Prunejuice would have nothing to do with such ordinary creatures at all, and every time our back screen door was left open, Prunejuice would make an effort to get into the kitchen. And if someone should rush to catch him while he was there, he would invariably try to get upstairs.

When he was two or three months old, Prunejuice decided he would learn to fly, and in a short time the highest chicken fence was no more than a low hurdle to him. Soon he began to follow Father to his work in the fields, as if he were somehow responsible for the crickets which he now began to find.

"Never saw a bird like him!" Father would say to the neighbors. "Sometimes you'd swear he was part human!"

But there came a day when Father wasn't quite so affectionate. One day Prunejuice was strutting around the back porch when a little sister gave a saucer of milk to the cat. Immediately Prunejuice too lay claim to it. There was a brief sound of battle, and suddenly the rooster rose in the air like a helicopter and descended into the half can of cream which was cooling in the water tank by the well.

"Upon my word I ought to drown you in it!" Father said as he rescued the spluttering bird. "I'll have to throw that cream to the pigs now!"

Which he did. And that night, somewhat regretfully I'm

sure, he chalked up the second entry in Prunejuice's account.

But two days later that same cat and the same rooster again had an argument, and before it was over there were two broken panes of glass in our hotbed cover. Then, late in August, Father backed the Model T out of the garage rather hastily one afternoon, and the ever-present Prunejuice got a leg under one wheel.

Father picked up his rooster and studied the dangling leg. "If you were my own, I'd just wring your neck," he said. "But seeing that you're the Lord's—well—well, what should I do anyhow?"

He had a word with Mother about that. "I hate to throw good money after bad," he said. "What do you think?"

The veterinarian had a good laugh that night when Father drove into town for his help. "I've prescribed for goldfish and canaries," he said. "But so help me Hannah this is the first time I've ever been asked to splice a rooster's drumstick!"

"I do feel awful silly bothering you about him," Father said. "But he is sort of special, you know."

When Prunejuice came back to the farm, he was shut up in the duckpen back of the woodshed to mend his leg and to make sure that he kept out of mischief. On occasion, however, when the day had a sun in it which was just right for a rooster to parade his colors, Father would give him the freedom of the yard again. Aside from such bright intervals as those, Prunejuice was a prisoner in the duckpen until the snow began to fly.

"Really don't know why we're keeping him," we heard Father saying to Mother one night when we were all around the lamp doing our homework. "Because he'll never amount to anything more than he is right now."

But we kept him nonetheless. And then one blustery night there was suddenly a great commotion at the window of our parents' bedroom. There was Prunejuice again, squawking as if a banshee was at his tail, and flapping his wings against the glass. Father opened the window and let him in.

"But I remember distinctly locking that duckpen door myself," he said. "Now how in the—?"

Quickly, Father slid into his trousers, picked his shotgun off the wall as he went through the kitchen and went outside. He was none too soon. The pair of young lads who had unlatched that duckpen door were just leaving. They had two of our ducks in a bag.

"We—we were just hungry, mister!" begged the older of the pair.

Father emptied the sack of its terrified booty and studied the shivering boys closely. He recognized them both, and so far as he knew, neither had ever been caught thieving before. And though both came from ne'er-do-well families, it was hard for Father to do the usual thing and call the constable. I think it was probably against his religion to take anyone to law.

"You're not working now?" he asked the older youth. "All right, I need some help in the bush right now. You report here tomorrow morning and cut wood with me and we'll say no more about this. . . . And you—" he said turning to the younger one— "you're supposed to be in school these days, aren't you? Only half the time you're playing hooky instead. Well, you just mind that I don't hear of you playing hooky any more if you don't want me to turn you in! Understand?"

The boys, sobbing with relief, went into the night. But bright and early next morning our new hired man timidly declared himself ready for work.

"Well, Mother," Father said, answering her indignant protest, "I think maybe he *was* hungry!"

The young lad, incidentally, stayed with us until the very last load of firewood came out of the woods that winter. "Come seeding time, I'd like to get that lad back," Father said when the boy finally left us. "Yes, sir, Prune-juice did us a mighty good turn that time! It's worth something to find a good hired man these days."

But how much was it worth? Father really had to decide before he could square things with the account on the back of the calendar. "Can't say that I feel quite right about adding up dollars and cents to prove your faith," he told Mother one night.

The account ran something like this now:

Expenses

Camp-meeting money	$5.00
Coal oil	.10
Half can cream all shot	3.25
2 panes glass busted	1.20
Veterinary — leg busted	1.00
Feed (app.)	.32

To the Good

Two ducks saved	$3.50
One hired man found	? ? ?

"Of course if you want to be exact there's still the worth of his carcass to be figured in. Shall we say five pounds at a quarter a pound? . . . But the arithmetic is still on the minus side!"

No, Father wasn't fond of this way of making God prove Himself at all. Not that he would believe for one minute that the Almighty couldn't prove Himself, but—

But it wasn't quite time yet to strike the final balance.

It was one bright morning in May when the big Pierce-Arrow drove into our lane. "You've got Dark Brown Leghorns here, I believe," the big man said. "Henry Becker tells me he sent you a setting last year."

"We didn't have very good luck," Father said. "We just raised one chick. A cock bird."

"Well, happens it's a cock bird I'm after really. I've got two dozen hens that's getting mighty lonesome. Where is he?"

"That's him over by the well trying to pick a fight with that tomcat," Father said.

We boys got Prunejuice in a corner, caught him and brought him over for the big man to examine.

"Aw pshaw!" our visitor exclaimed. "He's got a crooked leg!"

"I was going to warn you about that," Father said. "I ran over him once."

The man from the Pierce-Arrow puckered his lips. "Well," he said, lighting up a fresh cigar, "I was hoping to find a bird I could take to the shows too, you know. And this one would only be good for breeding. . . . Oh, I could offer you, say fifteen dollars if you're interested. . . ."

"Under the circumstances," Father said very quietly, "I doubt if I could refuse." He ran a hard but loving hand through the magnificent mahogany sheen of the rooster's hackle, and then bent over to nuzzle him against his cheek. "Good-by, Prunejuice!" he said

And when Prunejuice was ours no more, we thought that even the tomcat must have felt a little sad about it.

"Anyhow," Father said, "it's nice knowing he's going to a good home. And he's squared his account up so nice now too. . . . Let's see. . . . That leaves near eight bucks to the good now. . . . Plus the first five leaves— Means I'll have to put thirteen dollars in when they pass that basket again!"

But when camp-meeting time came round again, Father put in an extra five just to make sure.

Chapter 9

PREJUDICE HAS always been one of the uglier words of our language and we always resent having it applied to ourselves. It is always the unenlightened fellow down the road who is guilty of prejudice. Nor do we realize that prejudice is not always a sin against a color or creed but that its directions may be as varied as its dimensions.

We are aiming a lot of poetry and preaching against prejudice these days, and we need to. For we know now that prejudice—the other fellow's prejudice, that is—can sometimes black out the light like a hangman's hood.

But the sermon I shall remember longest was given me by my father, who in his own eyes, at least, was neither poet nor preacher.

I think I was twelve that year. It was the year when our family met Alfred Hurdy. We were at breakfast when the constable drove into the yard that morning and Father wondered what in the world the trouble could be.

"I think maybe you got a visitor somewhere on the premises," the constable said when Father went out. "Haven't seen him, have you?"

"And who would I be looking for?" Father asked.

So the constable told us the story then. "Alfred Hurdy is on the loose. Alfred Hurdy—that dummy Kurt Smith got up from the county farm, you know."

We knew of Alfred very well and we felt rather sorry for him. True, the poor fellow had never mastered the art of speech, but to our father that was scarcely reason for the popular supposition that he was "off in the head." One thing certain, he was smart enough to do a man's work. Kurt was just about the hardest man in the township to work for.

"He loose?" Father asked the constable. "Did Kurt fire him?"

The constable looked at Father closely. "I guess folks weren't too far off when they said Alfred was dangerous," he said. "It seems he gave one of Kurt's young lads quite a beating yesterday. He took that Charlie lad by the neck and was nearly shaking his head off when Kurt got to him. Of course, mind you, I'm not saying that Kurt's Charlie is any angel himself."

Father said, "He was probably teasing the life out of Alfred." We had all seen Kurt's boys abusing Alfred before.

"He's strong as an ox," the constable said. "I guess it will have to be back to the farm for him this time, Henry. Keep a sharp lookout for him, will you?"

It was our hired man Ralston who found him. He was over in one corner of our haymow, and he had been there all night. Even a child could have seen through his attempts to cover himself up. When the constable and his men came to take him, he stood up and offered no resistance as the handcuffs snapped over his wrists.

But Father, looking at the torn and shredded shirt, the thin pants and the trembling that filled them, could feel no thrill of adventure or victory. "Must be half frozen!" he said. "It was blamed cold last night."

"It's his own fault," the constable said. "Nobody asked him to run away. Anyhow he can get warmed up when he gets back to the county farm."

Alfred's sunburned face showed something close to terror when the constable mentioned the farm, and he shook his head vigorously.

"Get along now!" the constable warned, making a show of his gun. "No trouble with you!"

The constable stepped forward and took Alfred by the back. As he did so, one of the rents in the poor fellow's shirt widened into a flap. It was then that Father saw the welts.

Father looked at him. Alfred's was a simple face, but not a bad one really.

"If it's all right with you, Constable," Father said, "I'll send the young lad in to tell his mother to make a bit of warm breakfast. You're in no hurry to get him anywhere, are you?"

No, the constable was in no hurry. So they started off across the barnyard then, the four of them.

"Maybe you wouldn't mind if Alfred stayed with us a few days," Father said. "I don't think the county farm would care, do you?"

The constable and our hired man Ralston looked at each other in surprise. I remember that Ralston was a pretty hardheaded sort of fellow. I didn't like him too much because I had seen him beat the horses once. What made it seem all the worse to me was that he was supposed to be one of the Pepabun saints too, which is probably why Father had hired him.

"I've heard of people who kept pigs in the house," Ralston said. "Only I never did believe in it much."

"Better ask your wife about that, Henry," the constable suggested.

Mother was rather decent about it at first. She made Alfred a breakfast big enough for two that morning. She even got out a cake for him that she hadn't put on the table for ourselves. But when the meal was all ready, she brought it out into the woodshed and spread it on the table where Father kept such things as saw blades and old cans of nails.

"You can sit here," she told Alfred.

And while Alfred, freed of his handcuffs and all fear of the constable now, fell to his meal like a hungry animal, Mother went outside to do battle with Father.

"He's not staying!" she said. "Get that into your head! I won't have such a foul-smelling creature around the house!"

Ralston, of course, had to add his own gloomy weight to the argument. "And how would you feel if the poor brute took one of your kids by the neck and shook the daylights out of him, Henry?"

Father's words came even quieter than usual. "Well, there's an old Danish proverb I heard once, Ralston," he said. "Of course it's not exactly Scripture, but it's a proverb just the same. It says, 'In every man there is a king. Speak to the king and the king will come out.' "

Mother wasn't affected. "The answer is no, Henry! I won't have him around the place! I just couldn't!"

Father was a man who could neither do battle with his wife nor could he surrender a principle. So he just went out to the barn that day to let the thing subside.

But when Alfred, finished with his gigantic breakfast at last, came shuffling across the barnyard to join us and help with the work, Father asked him, "Would you like to stay for a while?"

Alfred's affirmative nod was so slight that the eye could hardly notice it, but the wreath of wrinkles on his peeling face made as strong a yes as if he had shouted it.

"Couldn't pay you much," Father went on. "But I could manage some clothes for you and somewhere to eat and sleep."

Alfred's smile broadened.

"Maybe we'd better go down to the store right away then," Father said, "and get you some decent clothes."

He got Alfred some soap and a couple of towels that day and when we got back he pointed out the place back in the creek where a summer bath was convenient and private. When Alfred hiked off over the field to find the recommended pond, Father went into the house to see Mother.

"I'll go halfway, Jeannie," he said. "If you make up his meals for him, I'll fix up the woodshed and he can stay out there."

Mother thought about it for a while, and then gave in. "All right," she said. "Fix up the woodshed."

So Alfred came to our woodshed, and if he had any bitter thoughts about his housing, he never let it show. He swept the dirt floor three times a day, he made his bed neatly every morning, and the few trifling possessions he gathered were stored immaculately in the orange box he invented for a cupboard. There was always a clean towel on the nail by the door. Alfred washed that towel himself every day. He kept it as clean as he kept himself.

And Alfred worked so hard that Father was a little ashamed. "Take it easy!" he said one day when he and Ralston and myself were all out hoeing. "You're doing as much as two men. You're not exactly paid to be a hired man, you know."

"Trying to show off," Ralston grumbled.

But Alfred only wrinkled his skull in his best-humored smile. If he heard Ralston, he didn't let on.

Alfred did everything that next week. He hoed, plowed, dug, picked stones, cut wood, made fences. And he always wanted to do more. "Kind of hard to understand a man that would take a fellow like that and try to squeeze even more work out of him," Father thought. He was thinking of Kurt, of course.

The constable came around one afternoon to see how things were going.

"Ralston's kind of got the wife worried about Alfred being dangerous," Father said. "What did the county farm say about him when you turned your report in?"

The constable spread his hands. "Well, they didn't seem to think that he was dangerous especially. Said they got along fine with him except that he was always restless for something to do and they didn't have much there that he could do. But they were pretty surprised to hear he'd been in trouble."

Perhaps it was because Mother refused to let us youngsters have much to do with him that Father brought the dog for Alfred. It was a rather yappy little mongrel Father got from one of the young barbarians down by the railway station.

When Alfred took the dog to his heart, Ralston's disgust deepened. "Mark my word," he declared ominously, "he's going to cut loose one of these days and hurt somebody."

Alfred did too. He cut loose on Ralston.

We heard the racket one noon hour when Father was allowing himself a few winks of sleep on the sofa behind the stove before going back to work outside. There was enough terrified racket in the noise to bring Dad out from his couch in a single leap.

Alfred gave his man one last shake and threw him on the grass beside the fence, as Father came out the door.

"Now then, what happened here?" Father asked.

"I told you what would happen," Ralston said as he shakily got up and dusted himself. "He's mad. Stark raving mad!"

"I asked what happened?" Father asked quietly again.

It was one of my younger brothers who first told the truth. "Ralston thought Alfred wasn't looking and he tied a tin can to the dog's tail," he said. "And Alfred got mad."

Father got out his handkerchief and wiped his nose. "You better get out to the fields, Ralston." Father went over to where Alfred was trying to get the can off his dog's tail and took the animal in his arms while Alfred worked the cord loose.

But Mother was more careful now than ever about letting Alfred near her children, and perhaps the fear would have grown into another rebellion if the baby hadn't stumbled into a bees' nest one afternoon. The child's terror was her best weapon that day because she could only holler and stand frozen to the spot. When Mother arrived, Alfred was already lugging the screaming child to safety. They counted at least eight stings on him later, but he only smiled. That night Mother went out to the woodshed with a new can of salve for Alfred's stings and an extra piece of pie for him.

"It does look pretty drab out there," she told the girls. "Maybe tomorrow we could find some old pictures we don't want and give him that old bureau with the drawers swelled shut."

They did a pretty attractive job on the place. They found an old carpet for the dirt floor, pictures for the walls, clean burlap for a ceiling and they loosened up at least two of the frozen drawers on the discarded bureau.

Father came by just as they were lighting a newly cleaned lamp on Alfred's table and complimented them on it. "It's not bad at all," he said. "Alfred's going to be mighty surprised when he comes back from the store tonight and sees all that. And I must say I'm a bit surprised myself. I just didn't think you liked him that much, Mother."

Mother suddenly became absorbed in the woodshed room again. "The table still looks bare, doesn't it?" she asked. "I wonder . . ." Without finishing she rushed into the house and came back with our own red and white tablecloth.

"Let him have this!" she said. "I'm getting tired of it anyhow."

When Alfred came back from the store he went out to the woodshed. A few minutes later, as they watched him from the kitchen window, Alfred came up to the back door and stood there as if afraid to knock. Father opened it for him. "Come in!" he said.

Hesitatingly Alfred came into the kitchen and when the light fell across his face they could see that his eyes were bright with tears. When Alfred noticed the bareness of our table he shook his head.

"He's trying to tell you that you shouldn't have done that," Father explained.

Alfred turned suddenly and went out through the back door. When he came back, the red and white checked tablecloth was in his hands.

"No! No!" Mother said. "It's for you, Alfred! I gave it to you!"

It took quite a little persuasion to make Alfred take the tablecloth back to the woodshed.

It was a Saturday, just an hour or so after dinner, when Art Bulwark telephoned our father. "This man of yours, the dummy, he's at my place, Henry. He's asking for a job. I was down at the store the other night telling the boys I was trying to find someone to clean out the bottom of my silo, you know, and I guess he heard me."

"If he wants to do the job, let him go to it," Ralston grumbled.

"But it's such a dirty job, Henry," Mother said. "It stinks worse'n boiled pigpen. He's likely to smell for two weeks afterward."

"Well, he's his own boss," Father said. "Maybe he wants to earn a little cash. I just give him a little pocket money here." Father said this over the phone to Art.

When he hung up the phone Father said, "Art says he'll give him five bucks for the job. I told him it was okay by me."

It was just a few minutes before supper that night when Alfred came up our lane looking like something the cat had dragged in. "My gracious, he's fallen in the creek, I think!" Mother exclaimed.

But Father knew better. Alfred had come home by way of the creek sure enough. But he had only tried to launder the smell from his newly acquired clothes before he presented himself at our back door.

Alfred rapped, and then when he heard us coming, he dropped his parcel and ran for the woodshed. It was Mother who opened the parcel. In it was a tablecloth from the store at the corner—the loveliest one they had there. She even remembered what it cost: five dollars.

After a while Father went upstairs and found a suit in the closet that he didn't wear very much. He came downstairs, and handed it to Ralston. "Take it out to Alfred," he said.

When Ralston returned he announced, "I guess the suit will fit all right, but it isn't exactly going to cover up that smell he's carrying around. Phew!"

It got strangely quiet in our kitchen. Mother took off the dishes which she had already laid on the table, unfolded the new tablecloth, spread it evenly and replaced the dishes. But when she got everything ready and it was time to sit down to it, she still hadn't managed any words. And on her face was a red that didn't come from mashing the potatoes.

"Well, heavens to Betsy!" Father said as he sat down at the end of the table. "If that wouldn't cork a duck now!"

We bowed our heads and waited for Father to say grace, but the prayer was so long coming I peeked up through my fingers to see what was wrong. Father was still looking at the tablecloth. Ralston, who was always impatient to start shoveling food, was looking up too. Finally all of us opened our eyes.

"It's no use!" Father said and he got up and went to the back door. "Alfred!" he called. "Come on in here!" Then to Ralston, "You move down one and leave a chair for him," he said.

So we waited until Alfred, awkward with gratitude and the new suit, came in for the chair beside Father. And then everything was all right, and Father's grace came out all right, and we ate.

Chapter 10

I T W A S O C T O B E R when old man Jarvis first introduced himself. He came up the road one morning leading
an old horse, only he wasn't leading it really, because when
the pair came close enough, we saw that there was no rope
between them. But they came in the lane cheek to cheek
almost, like old friends chatting, no hurry to either of
them. It didn't look like either of them was capable of
hurry any more.

"I heard about you down at the store," the old man said
when Father came out into the barnyard to meet him.
"I've just come to live with my daughter a couple of farms
down. Mrs. George Bagot. Know her?"

"Know her very well," Father said, not mentioning that
he knew her so well he was already feeling sorry for his
visitor.

Mr. Jarvis took a hank of hair that lay on the horse's
forehead and began twining it in his lumpy fingers. "This
horse," he said, "I—I guess I got to have him shot."

Father winced. "Your own horse?"

"Raised him from a colt. Been with me nearly thirty years now."

"He's been a good horse. I can see he's been used right too."

"Took him north to the lumber camp with me way back in '25. And he's been with me ever since. Used to bunk right up over the stable, you know. . . . They sort of pensioned us off a couple of weeks ago." The old man took a sugar cube from his pocket and the horse's pink lips quivered around till they found it.

"So you brought your horse back with you?"

"Well, he always was a great pet," Mr. Jarvis said as if to apologize. "You know how it is. Or maybe you don't. My daughter doesn't seem to. . . . Oh well, I'd of had to put him away before long anyhow. He's getting rusted up in his joints just like me. Had to help him up one morning."

There was a silence then that made us feel uncomfortable, because we knew that it came from the old man being afraid to talk about what was to come next.

Father reached out and took a fly that was coming up between the horse's front legs for his throat. "So your daughter doesn't want him around, is that it? Well, I wouldn't be in any hurry to shoot him. Why don't you leave him here for a while? For the summer, say."

"I can pay!" the old man said with pathetic eagerness. "I can pay a bit anyhow! Dollar a week, maybe. I've sort of promised my pension check for my board, you know, but I could sneak that much out to you. And I'll be out twice a day to sort of help look after him."

"Wasn't thinking too much about pay, Mr. Jarvis."

"Down at the store they were kind of laughing at you

being so soft on animals so I figured maybe you'd understand. His name's Barney."

"Glad to know you, Barney," Father said, scratching the horse's ears. "Now look, Jarvis, the best bit of pasture I've got left is that patch up on the gee side of the corn there. You take Barney out there and turn him loose."

So that was the coming of the horse. And along with him came a lot of ridicule and criticism too. We older boys ran our hands along his hollow back and knobby knees and said, "Now, Dad, if you had room for one more, why couldn't it have been a saddle horse?"

"All it can do is eat," Mother complained, "and there's not enough for our own this fall."

But it was Ralston, the hired man who was supposed to be one of the saints, who really took Father apart. "It's a sin," he declared grumbling as if to himself. "Downright sin to feed a useless critter when there's so many people that's hungry in the world. It's just not moral!"

Which had some good Christian logic in it, Father had to admit, and it bothered his conscience. But somehow he knew it would bother his conscience a lot more if he hurt either the old man or his horse. So he let Ralston's preaching go by along with all the other complaints.

"I always like to do the decent thing," he said quietly, "even when it doesn't seem to be altogether moral."

So every morning and every evening of that October, come rain, dew or dust, old man Jarvis came to visit his horse. He always came with sugar cubes and he always came out of breath from his haste. "I'd of been here sooner," he'd say. "Always did get up with the roosters, you know. Only I had to wait till I'd wiped the dishes. Seem a long time, Barney?"

Then he would give him the sugar. Sometimes he would let Barney eat from his hand, or he might lie on his back in the grass and let him pick the treat from his chest, or sometimes he might even let Barney pick it from between his own lips.

And more than once at such a time, we boys would snake on our bellies up through the long weeds that ran up to the pasture gate and lay there chuckling at the ridiculous sight. Father followed us with a handful of clods one day, and after he had flushed us out, he apologized for us.

"But it's all right!" the old man said. "It *is* a little crazy to be carrying on with a horse like this. But it's only for a week or two more."

One week went by. So did two of them. And one twilight around the end of the second one, the old man said, "Well, I guess it's about time now. First holiday he's ever had in his life but it's about time now. Only I haven't got a gun. You wouldn't want to do it for me, would you?"

Father shook his head. "Aw, let him stay where he is for a while," he said walking away. "Let him stay till it's time for stabling stuff. Grass is cheap."

So the old man went home whistling and patting his thighs with happiness that evening and Barney stayed on. October lived out its short, spicy weeks, and November blew in over the land in a rain so persistently cold that the cattle humped their backs and refused to take any further interest in the year at all. And then one day the breath of the north drifted in like a great white bird, bouncing sleet on the frozen ground and shriveling the last of the discouraged grass to its very roots.

It was time to bring the stock into the stable now. What about Barney?

"Well, I guess we better put him away now," Mr. Jarvis said the day they brought the stock in. "It's been a nice little stay for him out here, but it had to come to an end sometime. But could you do it for me?"

Father said he'd have to think it over.

He took his time about the thinking and the household got a bit impatient with him. And at breakfast one morning we boys said, "If we shoot Barney, we get the hide of him, don't we? Couldn't we get it tanned up into a robe?"

"Does seem like we've been good to that horse long enough now," Mother said. "The poor brute hasn't even enough spunk to hold up his head any more anyhow. Except when the old man comes, of course."

"If Jarvis is any kind of a man at all," Ralston said, "he'll let you sell that old critter for fox meat. Not that I've got any use for the raising of foxes, or for anything else that promotes vanity, but still, money is money."

And between the bunch of us we worked on Father until he had just about made up his mind that he might as well get the job done. Or have someone else do it. Ralston maybe. No, not Ralston. Well then, his brother George, the one who was supposed to be the spitting image of old Bill Green himself.

But when he went over to see our Uncle George about it, our uncle was just as reluctant as himself. "I know Jarvis," he said. "Too bad when a man gets as old as he is with nothing but a horse to put his love on. You won't miss the mite of hay he'll eat."

So Father went home as uncomfortable as ever, and not knowing what he would say when the old man came that evening for the last visit.

Father went out to the stable with him, nervous about

what kind of a scene there might be. But there was none. "It had to come anyhow," Jarvis said opening the small paper sack he always brought. "I couldn't have afforded what it would have been worth to stable him no-ways. Couldn't even have gone on paying the dollar a week I did for pasture. She makes me sign over my pension checks soon as they come now."

He upended the sack and a stream of sugar shot into his hand. "Can't even buy cubes any more," he said.

"Did you have to steal that?" Father asked.

"Some of it. Only she watches now. So I have to save it off my tea and porridge."

Father watched till the anger in his throat threatened to reach into his eyes. He watched the old man's tired hands gently follow the arch of Barney's glossy neck, or curling a wisp of mane about a finger like a mother would do with a baby girl. He had to get out of the way, so he picked up a pail of feed and went over to a sow which had begun to squeal indignantly for service. "Heavens to Betsy!" he mumbled. "A thing like this oughtn't to happen!"

So it didn't happen. When he came back to the stall he said, "Look here, Mr. Jarvis, my stable's going to be emptier than it should be this year. And a horse throws a good share of heat, you know. Why don't you leave him here to help keep the place warm?"

The old man went out into the dark of that November night with tears that the night couldn't hide. But they were good tears. Good enough to pay for Barney's winter board and then some, Father told us that night.

Around the stove after he had told what he had done, we started to scold him, of course. "My land, how long is this silly business going to go on?" Ralston asked as he pulled the best rocker up to the oven door.

"Maybe I'll leave that up to the good Lord," Father answered. "Maybe I'll board Barney till he just dies natural. Don't know for sure. But I'm going to be decent to that old man as long as I know it would bother me to be anything else."

"You're a richer man than I thought if you can afford to board a useless old rack of bones like that," Ralston said, almost under his breath.

But Father heard it and his voice snapped out of its usual patience. "A man can always afford to be decent," he said. "I'm pretty sure the Lord always sees to that."

So Father was decent all that winter. He gave Barney the same feed as his own horses got, and he made sure that the feeding was never left to Ralston. He helped Barney up in the morning sometimes when Barney's aging muscles seemed hardly equal to the job, and more than once when a storm kept his master from making his regular visit, and Barney would be whickering softly as he waited, Father would go into the house and get out a handful of sugar for him.

"Won't have too many chances to be good to him, I'm afraid," he said one night when one of the children asked him what he was doing with the sugar. "Getting a little harder every morning for Barney to get up. Wouldn't be surprised to go into the stable some morning and find out he'd just died in the attempt."

"Sooner the better," Ralston said.

But Barney did a surprising thing. As the grip of winter began to loosen, so did Barney's creaking joints. He got so spry that one day Father came into the barnyard to find three of us children riding him and doing acrobatics on his back. Best horse we ever saw for doing acrobatics, we said. You can trust him no matter what stunt you tried.

It was the old man that Time caught first.

There wasn't much warning. True, when January had choked the roads with snow and it took more energy than he could generate to make two trips a day, Mr. Jarvis began to come in the morning only. But for an old man with asthma and rheumatism, that was the only sensible thing to do.

But one morning long after the worst of winter was over and the ditches were sucking the last of the snow-water down from the slopes and the crows were noisily rowing back home again from the south, Barney whickered in vain for Mr. Jarvis and the little sack. And later in the day, when Father was driving down to the store with a case of eggs, he called in to see what was wrong.

"Nothing wrong with him much," his daughter said, holding the door open about as wide as she might for a Fuller Brush salesman. "Just a bit lazier than usual this morning and he didn't want to get up. Spring fever, I reckon."

She was a big, soft woman with little in her face to make a person want to know her, and much as Father wished to see his old friend that day, he didn't ask.

But the next day, he did. "I think your father would like to hear about his horse," he coaxed. "I won't stay long."

So, grudgingly, the woman opened the door and showed him into the room off the back kitchen where her father lay flushed and half asleep on an old army cot. Father shook the dirty covers and said, "How are you, Mr. Jarvis?"

Mr. Jarvis opened his eyes briefly, recognized nothing and went back to sleep.

"He's pretty stupid today," the daughter said. "Not that he's ever too bright."

"Barney was asking for you," Father said.

The tired eyes fluttered open and this time they saw. "Barney? How's Barney?"

"How are you? That's the big question."

"I'll be all right, Henry. I just take it by spells, that's all. But I've had them before. If I can just get through April, I'll be all right."

The daughter just smiled about that. "Always had that crazy superstition that he was going to die in April," she said. "Just because his parents both died in April. Ever hear of anything so nuts?"

"But how's Barney?"

The daughter went out then, shaking her head and muttering as if this business about Barney was just too nuts for her to endure. And Father and Mr. Jarvis talked about Barney till Father thought the old man should go back to his rest. "Tell you what," he said as he got up to leave, "tomorrow I'll bring Barney down with me. I'll bring him right outside the window there and you can take a good look at him. Would that be okay?"

It was so okay that the old man began to cry a little.

So next day Father brought Barney down the road and stood him in the garden outside the room. The daughter was in rare good humor that day.

"Barney, Barney, Barney!" she said as Father went through the house to open the window. "That's all I heard all night long. My stars and garters, it seemed to me he was doing just about everything with that horse! One time he was a breaking him in when he was a colt. And another time, I'll be go to grass if he didn't seem to be helpin' him down out of a tree or something. And bandaging up his leg. And talking to him as if he was a kid in a crib. You can imagine how much sleep I got."

Father fought back his anger, felt the old man's brow

and helped him up to look out the window. Then he put the sugar cubes he had brought into the withered palm and drew Barney's attention to it. Barney whickered and took the sugar and kissed him a dozen times for it. And that was about all there was to it except that the horse nearly put his nose through the glass when the daughter came in to put the window down.

Father didn't notice the envelope which had been shoved into his jacket pocket until after the chores that night. The envelope was sealed. On the outside, the shaky writing said, "Henry, if I cross over you read this but please not before."

"I wonder what's in it!" Mother exclaimed. "Suppose it could be some money?"

"Fat chance," Ralston said.

Father didn't have long to wait before he could open the letter, because next morning the daughter was ringing the phone off the wall to tell us that her darling, darling father had passed on. Found him dead in bed. Didn't give them any notice at all. Why, it couldn't have been any more than an hour or two before that when he was raving about that fool horse just as loud as ever. And then she began to wail.

"You'd think she had a heart and it was busted into smithereens," Father muttered as he told the news to the family.

And that day he went out to the stable, out to Barney's stall, and opened the letter. It read:

it's too far from the end of april and I don't think I can make it henry. now henry you'll be putting barney away now, too bad he couldn't of had just one spring with no work but there's just one think I'd like to ask you to make a little funeral for barney before you cover him up, maybe you could make his grave in some nice place by a crick or a tree and then read a little verse or say something nice about him for a sort of good-by. because they say there's no afterward for a horse so I think he at least ought to have a nice good-by said.

by the way henry there's an old chaindrive clock you'll see in the kitchen. it come from ireland with my mother and it's not much but it's all I got and I want you to have it so you take it when I'm gone.

Father wouldn't tell what the letter said for almost two weeks because it didn't seem right that anyone should laugh at a man so soon after he had passed on, even if he was rather childish. But finally one night we made him show it to us.

"The poor lonely man!" Mother said. "I'm so glad you didn't listen to me when I scolded you, Henry. The poor old fellow!"

"That reward you were supposed to get to show that the Lord approved," grunted Ralston as he pulled off his boots for his hour at the oven door, "doesn't seem it's showed up yet, does it?"

"Which reminds me, Jean," said Father patting her on the shoulder, "Jarvis left that old clock to us. How be you pick it up next time you're down that way?"

We never got the clock. Mother came back mad enough to chew nails. "Why, that old wretch!" she cried. "She won't give us the clock! Says she's got a right to what little he left to help pay expenses. And you know what? She says they're coming to get the horse too. They're going to sell it for fox meat."

"Uh-huh," Ralston grunted, making it sound like "I told you so."

"They won't take the horse," Father promised quietly. "I'll handle that end of it. And I guess I better get it over with first as well as last. This afternoon, I guess."

Mother wilted a bit when she saw him getting the shotgun. "But there isn't any point in keeping him any longer, is there?" she asked. "Not now."

"No," Father said. "Not now, I guess. Only, like the old man said, it would have been kind of nice if Barney could have had just one spring without work. . . . You phone George to come over this afternoon, will you? . . . And, Ralston, when you go down to the store at noon, just sort of pass the word around to any of the boys down there that mightn't be doing anything this afternoon."

Ralston said, "I don't approve of this. Looks like a plain mockery of Christian burial, that's all. One thing sure, I'm not going to take part in it."

"You're at least going to help shovel the dirt in," Father promised him.

He turned to us boys then. "And you lads go drag that canvas tarpaulin down from over the drive-shed. Seems to me it would be more respectful if we had something to cover Barney over with while the funeral was going on. And don't you try following me, either. For a dirty job like this I don't want anyone around at all."

There must have been little else to do in the vicinity that afternoon because a lot of men came up for the funeral. There were even a couple of men that Father could never remember seeing before. Seemed like almost everyone around had come except Geordy Bagot, the son-in-law who was supposed to be confiscating the horse.

Father had everything ready by the time they got there,

and everything was as dignified as he thought Mr. Jarvis would have wanted it. He had the grave dug, and the big inert form of Barney, properly shrouded over with the tarpaulin, lay beside it. A little sheepishly, he started the rites.

"I'm not saying that this is altogether a sensible thing to do," he admitted. "But I don't figure it hurts to carry out a lonely old man's last wish, even if it does seem a little silly. And maybe it's not silly anyhow. Maybe it's just silly to us."

Some of the men at the back began to laugh about something and Father waited. "I was going to see if I couldn't hunt up a little text about a horse somewhere, but it took me so long to dig this grave that I didn't get around to it," he said. "Anyhow it seems to me that the Bible always seemed to be speaking about asses instead of horses, so I cut me this little verse about how faithful a horse can be out of the Almanac."

But Father couldn't find the verse. He fumbled in every pocket, in his wallet, in his hatband. Finally, red-faced and nervous, he turned to Ralston. "Maybe you could give us something," he begged. "Just say something."

So Ralston took on steam and gave forth. "I think Henry was right when he said that this was all a bit silly. The horse was given to man for man's use and when that use is finished, man has every right to dispense with him. We've got no license to be cruel, of course, but . . . why, right in the very first chapter of the Bible it says that God gave man dominion over every living thing on earth. And a horse has no soul, we all know that. So while we should be thankful for being given the use of this animal and all that, I think that this here getting sentimental about him is just—"

Uncle George's voice cut in like the crack of a whip. "Shame on you!" he cried, shaking his finger at Ralston. "All I got to say is that if a horse doesn't have a soul he's sure got a lot more right to one than many of them that's reputed to own them!"

"Blasphemy!" Ralston said. "Sacrilege!"

"Whether it's blasphemy and that other word or not, a horse does what he does just for the pure sake of being faithful. Do you? Would you be so holy if you didn't see any reward attached to the end of it somewhere?"

Uncle George wiped the blush of temper off his face. "Funny piece of business," he went on, "a man works forty hours a week for forty or fifty weeks of the year in some nice warm place, and when he gets too old he's pensioned off so he can go to some nicer and warmer place. You kick a man in the scullery someday for loafing on his job and you'll get thrown in the clink with a whole union sitting on the lock. That's just Christian justice and enlightenment, we say. But a horse, well, you can keep a horse in the harness from sunup till the last fiddler goes home, feed him anything the cows won't eat, bust a rail over him if he doesn't pull hard enough and shoot him any old time you like. That's supposed to be Christian justice too, says Ralston here. . . . Well, all I got to say is that if a man sees fit to pension off a good horse and give him a little time to soak up the sun before it sets on him, I say he oughtn't to be called silly or something worse!"

It was a real good funeral, everybody said as they started home. Best one they'd ever been at. Only Ralston, still smarting from the humiliation he had received, had to have something dark to say.

"You ever figure out all the money that this old critter has cost you?" he asked as they started dragging the tarpaulin back to the house. "You ever figure out just how much money you could of saved for the family, or for good books, or the collection plate?"

Whether he was supposed to or not, our Uncle George heard the holy rumblings and he edged Father off to one side of the lane to say a word or two to him in private.

"I'd say your hired man's head is considerable bigger than his brain is, Henry! Or his heart either, for that matter."

"He does get stubborn and trying at times," Father admitted.

"Isn't it a great shame now that our old man couldn't have been here today to help us take him down a notch?"

"Could be I'm not working him hard enough," Father said.

Which suddenly reminded Uncle George of one of the old-time remedies that their father sometimes used to prescribe for swollen heads when they were boys back home. "Do you mind, Henry, how he used to tell us that there was nothing any better for what ailed us than to have to fork good ripe pig manure for about eight hours on a windy day? Mind that?"

Father turned his face around to sniff the wind. "That breeze could be stiffer," he said, beginning to smile. "But I guess it would do all right. And come to think of it, my pile of pig dung is nearly up to the edge of the roof now. . . ."

The two Green brothers, now become boys again, enjoyed a mysterious chuckle together, but by the time Father reached the house and gave Ralston his rugged assignment, his face was quite serious again. Not as serious as that of Ralston, though, when Father couldn't be convinced that this was a job that could wait.

I think it was as near to revenge as Father ever allowed himself in all the years we knew him.

Chapter 11

"If there's anything I can do! Anything at all!"

And we say those words in all honesty, wishing till our tears get in the way that there might be something—something that we could do for that neighbor whose door has just known the shadow of death. But we know all too well that there is nothing we can do that will be anything more than a gesture. We may help with the chores perhaps, or send some baking to the stricken house, or extend the welcome of our roof to the funeral visitors.

But as for the grief itself, there is little that we can do or say. We may offer a line of poetry or a scripture verse or a prayer, but the hope which goes out with such offerings seems such a desolate one.

I hear you say that it must always be so?

Before you tell me that nothing else is possible—that death must always seem as deaf and merciless as a stone Christ in a cemetery—I should like to tell you about Father and Bill McGuigan.

In the old home town he was known as Duckfoot Bill, a name he had to endure along with many another bit of teasing from the villagers up the hill from his tarpaper shack. If you wanted to be brutally frank about it, you could have said that both Bill and his wife were a little crazy. If you were kinder, you would merely explain that they were both quite harmless, but a little odd.

I remember that as young barbarians, we would follow Bill as he would waddle up toward the main street for the mail or a few groceries or a plug of smoking tobacco for Daisy's clay pipe. And we had a song we had made up for just such an occasion:

> Down by the Dooley bridge
> Down past the mill
> There lives old Daisy
> And her Duckfoot Bill
> His last hind leg is longer
> Than it really ought to be
> 'Cause she yanked him at the ankle
> And loosed him at the knee.

Bill was a big, red-faced man who always had a feather of some kind caught behind the snap of his greasy peaked cap. He had too much flesh on him, and as he propelled his bulk along the street he would swing his left leg around in an awkward arc, as if it were wood from the hip down.

"Daisy been pullin' your leg again lately, Duckfoot?" we would call. "Been makin' any more muskrat stew, Duck-foot?"

To which Bill would ponderously wheel in his tracks, take off his cap as if to bat us with it, and then delight us with the most colorful swearwords which have ever adorned a temper.

"Is it right that old Daisy whaled you with the poker for drinkin' up all her dandelion wine, Duckfoot? . . . Is it right that she put a piece of horse hoof into your barrel of cider to give it a little kick, Duckfoot?"

They had their tiffs all right, but I am sure that few of these were quite so dramatic or picturesque as the accusations we shouted at his back. For everyone knew that the pair were inseparable. When it was flax-pulling time and the mill posted its annual advertisement for workers, Daisy and Bill bent to the job together, never quite agreeing on anything, but never more than a pace or two apart. If it were the time of year for trapping again, Daisy would follow the creek along with her man. If there were leeks or berries or mushrooms in the woods, it was an expedition for both. So was fishing. So was hunting.

"Aw, give me that there rifle!" Daisy would say, a smile of derision cracking her homely Irish face. "Give me that there rifle and I'll show you how to pick the eyetooth out of a sparrow!"

Everybody knew that she could shoot better than Bill could. Everybody but Bill. That was one of the things he and Daisy were always arguing about.

Where they came from, I never really knew and it is too late to ask now. They seemed to have been there since the beginning, like the creek which lapped at their door, or the bridge beyond. I cannot imagine them ever having visitors. They never asked for help. For all our cruel pretensions at familiarity, none of us ever really knew them. We only knew they lived in a world of their own, a curious little world beyond the edge, and that they had nothing but each other.

And then, through the black fog of a November dawn,

Bill came up the hill to pound on the doctor's door. "You've got to come with me, doctor!" he said. "I can't wake Daisy up!"

The village council provided the funeral, complete with a satin-lined coffin and a minister. And when it was finally time to ease the box into the old horse-drawn hearse and someone tried to help Bill into the first buggy behind, he still couldn't believe what had happened.

"Wait!" he said, trying to get down again. "I've got to go back and get Daisy! She's still in bed!"

Some of the church ladies got together that night and agreed that Bill surely ought to be taken to an institution now. It was even dangerous having him wandering about half out of his head. Couldn't something please be done about it?

A day or two later, however, the council was able to reply that Bill must have regained at least a part of his comprehension because one could see him almost any hour of the day now sitting on Daisy's grave.

And now the village which had so long made Bill its jester suddenly discovered a lump in its throat. Old clothes and baskets of victuals and even offers of work found their way to the shack by the creek. At our place we happened to kill a pig a few days after Daisy was buried; and when the women had finished the sausage making and a considerable portion of these had been set aside as our usual fall gifts to such people as our Uncle George, Grandma, the new young preacher at Pepabun, Father Kelly and the Methodist minister downtown, Father said: "Now maybe you'd make up a smaller parcel for old Bill. Better throw in a few pork chops too, hadn't we?"

I went to town with Father that morning and when we stopped in to see Bill, he was sitting head down beside a table which was heaped with unopened groceries.

"Just thought you might like some of these here sausages of ours, Bill," Father said.

Bill scarcely nodded.

"Would you like something to read, Bill?" Father said after an awkward pause. "Maybe you'd have a look at these sometime." I saw then that Father had brought some of his precious *Gospel Trumpet* magazines, which he generally saved till they got yellow.

There was still no sign from Bill. The fire was nearly out, and Father went outside and split an armful of wood and set the stove ablaze again. "Bill," he said in a voice I scarcely recognized, "if there's anything I can do for you! Anything!"

Then just as we were going out the door, Bill suddenly came to life. He got up and came halfway across the kitchen as if he had just thought of something. Then he shook his head, and when we said good-by, he was back in his chair again.

"Foolish me and them magazines!" Father said when we were climbing the hill into town. "Why, I don't even know whether Bill can read or not. Likely not!"

When the minister came to his door for his sausages that morning, Father had a request to make of him. "I'd sure like it if you'd manage a visit to old Bill," he said. "He must be awful lonely and there's just nothing I can seem to say to him."

But the minister gave something less than a promise and I could see that Father wasn't too happy about it. He always had been a little doubtful about that minister. He was too comfortable.

Next Sunday afternoon, Bill came lumbering up our lane. He had walked all the way. "Come in and set, Bill!" Father exclaimed. "We were just going to have supper!"

But no amount of coaxing could make Bill sit down with us to a meal. One thing that even the Ladies Aiders had to admit was that whatever else one might say about Bill's judgment, he certainly knew his place. "No, Henry," Bill said. "I—I just wondered if I could have a private word with you somewheres."

Father took Bill into the parlor and closed the door so we children could only guess at what was happening. I was almost a man before I was allowed to know.

"Henry," he began that night, "I wanted to ask you about what that preacher was saying at the funeral. Is it really true, Henry, about heaven and all that?"

"As sure as I'm sitting here, Bill, it's true," Father replied. "Oh yes indeed, it's true!"

"I reckon I never thought much on it myself, Henry. Not till now anyways."

Father, though he was quiet almost to the point of shyness about his faith, had to confess it boldly now, to show the light to a soul in darkness. "Bill," he said fervently, "I'm as sure as anything that you could see Daisy again someday. . . ."

But Bill soon set him right about that. "Henry," he said, "you've got no idea at all of what kind of man I am. I reckon you never knew any man in your whole life as low as me. . . . Daisy now—well, Daisy was always different. If she didn't make it to heaven I reckon they might just as well plow the place up and plant it in potatoes because they'll never be needin' it for nobody."

Father must have wrestled mightily for Bill's soul that Sunday, but all to no avail. "Me, I was born a wrong one and there's nothing could ever change me, Henry. Even Daisy couldn't change me none, and she was forty-two years tryin' it. . . . Anyhow, Henry, that wasn't what I come here for. Not exactly. You see—well, just the night before she died, when we were playin' euchre, I got awful mad at her. Oh, I called her everything I could think of! I told her I wished I'd never met her! I was so mad at her I slept on the couch that night. And then next morning . . ."

Father had to wait a little.

"All I want to do now, Henry," Bill went on, "is to send Daisy a message. And I reckoned you'd be the one man around that might have a mind to help me. Would you?"

Father couldn't understand at first, but it was remarkably simple when Bill explained it. "I know you go visiting people a lot, Henry—people that's down like I was and people that's sick. . . . Now look, you must know somebody that's going to pass over pretty soon, somebody that's been decent enough to make it through all right. Why couldn't I send a message with somebody like that?"

Father thought it over. "Well, Bill, there's old Mort Gillespie up the center side road. He says he's going any time now. What's your message, Bill?"

Two nights later Father hitched the colt to the light wagon, drove down to the shack on the creek for Bill and then out to the side road to the place where Mort Gillespie was gallantly fighting out his last few days. Mort and Father were both chicken fanciers and they had been good friends ever since I could remember.

"No regrets," Mort greeted that night. "No regrets at all. It's been a good life mostly. By the way, Henry, do I owe you anything? Been trying to decide if I don't owe you a setting of hatching eggs. Do I?"

"No," Father told him. "You don't owe me anything.

But you've got an awful good Campine rooster going to waste out there in the orchard right now that I'd like to have. That daughter of yours will only pot him as soon as you're gone."

"Welcome," said Mort. "Catch him and take him! He took first at Mount Forest two years in a row, that bird did."

"I've got Bill McGuigan here," Father finally explained. "He's got a favor to ask. He's still pretty broke up about losing Daisy, you know. And he wonders if you'd mind hunting her up when you cross over. He's got a message for her."

"You'll find her easy," Bill said. "She's bound to be down by a creek somewheres. That's the first place she always headed for whenever she had to be alone. Down by the creek."

"I'll be glad to look her up," Mort said quietly. "I don't guess I'll be particularly pressed for time. What's the message, Bill?"

It wasn't too easy for Bill to get it out. "Just tell her that I—that I didn't mean it," he said.

He took out his dirty bandanna then, blew his nose a time or two, tried his best to think of some better way to word this last and most important communication. "No, I reckon that'll have to do," he said at last. "Just tell her that I didn't mean a word of it, that's all."

"I imagine I'll see her before the week's out," Mort said. "If you think of anything else in the meantime, let me know." And he began to cough and get gray then, so his daughter came into the bedroom to take over and they had to go.

True to his promise, three nights later Mort departed with his message. And the next time Father and I saw old

Bill climbing up toward the main street again, he seemed almost himself again.

"Thanks for them sausages, Henry," he said. "Best I ever tasted. . . . Would there be anything I could do for you sometime, Henry? Anything at all?"

Chapter 12

WE WHO ARE old enough now to boast of being sadder and wiser, are apt to tell our adolescents how wonderfully lucky they are to be so young. "Why aren't you happier?" we ask. "Don't you know you're living the best days of your life right now?"

I suspect, however, that few of us really believe that. Or if we do, it is because we have made ourselves forget the tears of our childhood, and the many lonely battles which had to be lost before we could come to man's estate. It is ironic, perhaps, that of all the lonely battles of my own youth, the one which can still recall a tear to my throat should have happened on Father's Day—a day which invites the family to be closer and happier than usual. It is even more ironic because that battle was fought with my father, who was as fine a parent surely as any man who ever sat at the head of a table.

It started, in a way, with the Father's Day program which our Sunday School was planning. To us children the idea for that program was unusual enough to be quite exciting, though the project itself was really very simple. Come the big morning of that day, each youngster in the class who was able to push a pencil was supposed to get up in front of the assembly and read a short essay on the subject: *What Kind of Man My Father Is.*

The fathers, of course, were supposed to be present along with any other adults who wanted to share the fun.

There was more than the usual amount of scribbling at our house because there were three of us who had elected to write our father's biography. My younger brother seemed to be having the most trouble of all of us with his effort. With the awkwardness of his seven years he had so far printed but four wobbly lines:

My father's name is Henry. He is 38. He likes horses. He only sold one horse. It stepped on his foot three times so he sold it. He . . .

We weren't supposed to know what was in that note, for my brother guarded it fiercely, but one night when we were all supposed to be asleep, my mother found it hidden in an old shoe and she read it to Father. By putting my ear to the stovepipe hole I could hear her very plainly.

"Well," Mother laughed as she showed Father the note, "at least he did it all himself!"

My sister, who was a romantic nine that year, had a little more to show for her talent:

My father is a farmer but he is good-looking. Even my mother thinks so. He doesn't talk much but he sings nice. Most people like my father very much and are always borrowing money and things from him. My father hardly ever gets mad at people even when Mama tells him to. . .

Mother was pretty proud of that effort. She thought her daughter could read character amazingly well.

"Sure, Mama, it's just that the girl has a bit of her mother's blarney, that's all!" Father told her.

But as for myself, I hadn't written my essay, nor was I in any hurry to do so. At least I was in no hurry to write any such paragraph of praise as my brother and sister had managed. For all that week I had been nursing a grudge against my father. So far I had been rather decent about it, I thought. I had kept my righteous indignation pretty much to myself, but by the end of that week I was determined that I wouldn't keep the peace much longer. I had been patient enough with my father.

The reason for the disagreement was simply that I had planned to sleep outside with the Armbruster boys that Saturday night, and Father wouldn't let me. We had been planning that adventure for several weeks. We had spent a whole weekend making a tent out of grain sacks; we had scrounged enough old blankets and quilts, and we had enough money now for buns and wieners. To be deprived now of the required permission seemed outrageous.

Even Mother thought that Father was being too strict with me. "After all, it isn't as if he were hitchhiking or something," she told Father. "They only want to go down the creek a ways."

But Father told her what he had already told me a dozen times. "It's just that those lads he's running around with right now aren't the kind I want him to be alone with at night, Mother," he explained. "Those Armbruster boys have been into altogether too much trouble lately to suit me. I think it's enough if I let Gordon play with them where I can keep an eye on them. And I think Gordon is old enough now to understand that!"

So that Saturday evening, when even Mother couldn't move him, I was really furious. "You're sure going to be sorry for being so mean to me like this!" I told him. "I'll never forgive you!"

Father was just sitting down to start supper when I said that, and I remember that he looked up at me for what seemed a long time without saying a word. Then he said, "I'll tell you what I'll do. I'll go halfway about this. I'll let you sleep out if you'll watch that old sow in the stable tonight. We could move a bed into the alleyway, you know."

"You must be crazy!" I stormed. It was a very daring thing to call your father crazy when I was a boy.

"If your friends would promise me not to smoke, I'd let them sleep in the stable with you," Father went on evenly.

I could hardly believe my ears. "You want me to sleep in a dirty old pigpen?" I repeated.

Father seldom lifted his voice at a time like this. "Somebody's got to do it," he said.

I was so angry now the tears flew to my eyes. "I'm not sleeping in any old pigpen!" I cried. "Why can't I be like other boys anyhow? Does Mr. Armbruster boss his kids like you do?"

Father said, "I guess I just happen to be different, Gordon. And you just happen to be stuck with me for a dad, that's all. Now let's eat."

But I had no intention of eating. All that I wanted to do now was to fight through to this battle's bitter end. "I'm going to go anyhow!" I shouted. "And you're not going to stop me! If I'm old enough to do so much work around here, I guess I'm old enough to have fun once in a while!"

My father caught me just as I strode angrily out through the back door. "You're getting altogether too big for your britches, lad!" he said. "Now you go upstairs to your room.

I'll be up to see you later. After I've cut me a good switch!"

As I look back upon such uncomfortable moments now, I am convinced that Father administered a whipping only when he was absolutely sure that duty left him no other choice. And even then the strokes were very few because there was never any temper in him when he got around to the actual punishment.

I wonder now if a harder licking that night might not have conquered me. As it was, I came through that ordeal in the bedroom with more rage and determination in me than ever. "I hate you!" I screamed at him. "You're the meanest man I ever saw! And people think you're so awful nice too! Huh! Well how would you like it if I told them the truth? How would you like it if I told them at Sunday School tomorrow what kind of a father you are? Well, that's just what I'm going to do! You'll see!"

I shrieked at him as he went down the stairs and didn't let up till he closed the hall door between us. Then I went over to the stovepipe which came up through my bedroom from the kitchen below and I listened carefully to see what he was going to say to Mother about me. But all I heard was Mother's voice. "Henry!" she was pleading gently, "please don't bother about those pigs tonight! You look so tired! Please lay down for a spell!"

"Don't worry about me," Father said. "I'll take a cot and a blanket. I just can't afford to take a chance on those little beggars getting laid on. Maybe by tomorrow night I can trust the old sow to manage them herself."

"But you've already got a cough, Henry!" I heard Mother protesting as she followed him to the back porch.

Now, as I think back on that time, I can scarcely believe that I could have been so devoid of all pity, or so determined to have my revenge. But in one fiercely triumphant moment I had the plan of that revenge all completed. The Armbruster boys were to meet me at nine in the tent by the creek, and whether my father said so or not, I would meet them there. With Father busy out in the stable, it would be the simplest thing in the world to slip down the drainpipe from my bedroom window as soon as it was dark enough.

In the meantime, while I was waiting for the dark to come, I would write that essay I had warned him about and have it all ready to take to Sunday School next morning.

Somehow, by the time I found pencil and paper, the essay I had originally planned didn't seem to be quite right. But then just as I had almost decided not to write the essay at all, I remembered that my rebellion would probably earn me another trimming when I got back home in the morning and that renewed my bitterness.

So I wrote it, and it went something like this:

What Kind of Man My Father Is

My father is the most old-fashioned father I ever met. He is always so sure he knows just what is right but he thinks his kids never do. He doesn't seem to think that there's times when a guy should be let to live his own life like other dads do. He is also old-fashioned about work. He thinks kids today ought to work as hard as he did when he was a boy. Last night he even wanted me to sleep with a bunch of little pigs so I could keep their mother from laying on them. He's very old-fashioned about punishment too. He is the only father I know who doesn't think a boy eleven years old isn't too old for a switching. I'm afraid some boys would find my father hard to get along with. . . .

There now, I thought, reading it over for effect, was something restrained enough to read in Sunday School—after all, you *were* supposed to tell the truth in Sunday School, weren't you?—and yet there would be just enough edge to it to shame my father in front of all the people who thought him so perfect.

I folded the paper carefully, tucked it into the inside pocket of my Sunday jacket and lay back on my bed to wait for the last bit of western sky to darken into night. But as I waited, a twinge of discomfort crept into me. Come to think of it, maybe that wasn't quite the kind of essay one dared read at a Sunday School. Certainly it wouldn't be the kind the superintendent was expecting.

I still was positive that every word of it was true, mind you, yet something began to tell me that it wouldn't be right to read it in public.

Suddenly I had a great idea. I would leave the essay on my bureau, face up, as if I hadn't expected anyone to notice it. They would, of course. One of my brothers or sisters would see it as soon as the family climbed the stairs to go to bed, and after that it would be no time at all until the paper was shown to my father.

"Then he'll tear it up!" I thought exultantly. "And I can blame him for not having anything to read to-morrow!"

It would be revenge enough just to have him read it!

That night's tenting expedition was a dismal failure. The Armbruster boys scolded me for being late and for not bringing anything to eat. Then the fire didn't want to go, and when it did, the smoke blew right into the tent. The Armbrusters began rolling cigarettes then, and one of them burned a hole in the good blanket I had smuggled out of my bedroom window with me.

Then about eleven o'clock a wind blew up, and it was cold and full of rain. The grain sacks in our tent were far from windproof.

It didn't take my friends long to make their decision. "Let's get out of here!" they said and off they went. But I, who wanted to go home far more desperately now than they did, had to stay. Whatever it was I was trying to prove demanded that I stay.

I suppose that it must have been past midnight when my father came. I could hear his footsteps long before he got to the tent and I knew who it was by the way he would cough now and then. I wasn't asleep, far from it, but I pretended I was. Well, I thought, if he's going to lick me now at least it will be over with and I can get home.

But when there was no voice to wake me to my fate, nor any hard hand on my shoulder, I opened my eyes ever so slightly and saw that my father had brought a canvas tarpaulin with him, and that he was quietly draping it over the sapling frame of the tent. Then, when he had it in place, he knelt down in the wet grass, and reaching in through the flap, he very softly put another blanket over me.

The last thing I heard as he started back to his lonely vigil in the stable was his cough. It was three-quarters of a mile back home.

Next morning when I got back to the warmth of our kitchen, very early, neither of us spoke. I think Father was watching me closely, but I didn't have the courage to look back. He didn't speak to me in fact until we were all in the Model T and on our way to Sunday School. "Got your essay all ready, lad?" he asked.

"Oh jeepers!" I exclaimed as if I meant it. "I plumb

forgot! I left it laying on my bureau!" Which indeed I had.

Then, just as I settled back thinking that everything was going to be all right after all, Father put his hand in his pocket and handed me the essay. "Lucky I happened to see it," he said.

I wanted to burst into tears. I wanted to tear the hateful paper to bits and scatter it in the wind. But I couldn't do that. I still had too much pride. What *could* I do then?

That Father's Day program drew almost as many people as our Christmas tree might have, and nobody who came was disappointed. The essays were surprisingly entertaining, and the fact that some had obviously been touched up by the hand of some conniving mother didn't seem to detract from the fun in the least. One grinning little miss even admitted such help when she read:

"My mama says that on Father's Day we should all go on a picnic to the zoo, and then we should choose up sides and throw stones at the stork. . . ."

My brother David had finally added another line to his ponderous bit. The line read: "When Mom isn't looking, he steals cake for me sometimes."

My sister hadn't changed hers much. She had merely summed everything up by a final line which said: "My father is cute and he is nice. Everybody says so."

As for me, however, these were things to laugh about long afterwards. At the time they happened I was far too miserable to be touched by any wit or jollity. Besides, I was far too busy writing—scratching out—writing again.

. . .

By the time my name was called, however, I had finished with it. Would I be able to get it out of me?

First, I read the part I had written the night before. I didn't change a word of it. I looked up once and saw Father in the back row with his head in one hand and looking at the floor. I shouldn't have seen him like that. It made it awfully hard to read what I had written on the back. Which was something like this:

"At least that's the way it used to seem to me. Only last night, after my father and me had a fight about all of these things I got mad and called him names and ran away on him. I figured maybe I'd make him feel sorry and ashamed of himself. Only in the middle of the night it began to rain, and he came all the way down from the stable to cover me up and fix the tent with a tarpaulin to keep it dry. Even though he was tired he did it. Even though I said I hated him. . . . And he had a cough. . . . And when I heard him coughing, I—"

To save my life I couldn't seem to get hold of the next word, and the superintendent looked over my shoulder to see if I had something in my essay that was too big for me to pronounce.

Finally I got it out of me. "I sort of changed my mind," I said. Then I gave up and went back to my seat.

It took me a little while after that to look over to my father's row, and when I did, he wasn't there. After a bit I got up and went outside and there he was on the walk by the church door looking way up at something which seemed to be at the other end of the street.

I went over and stood beside him but he didn't say a word and he didn't make a move. He just kept looking up the street.

At last I said, "About those pigs, Dad, if it's all right with you, I'll look after them tonight."

He put his hand on my shoulder then and smiled a little. But we didn't go back into the Sunday School. We just got into the Model T and waited for the others.

Chapter 13

I AM A CHICKEN FANCIER, one of those strange, mash-marked men you will find joyously camped between the rows of feathered bedlam in the poultry section of almost any fair. We are strange, I say, because ours is a hobby that few can ever understand. The breeders who raise other kinds of livestock are sane enough. The animal of their choice generally earns them a living. But ask a man of the "fancy" how much money his birds pay him per year and if he gives you an answer at all, don't expect it to be the truth. His wife may tell you, however, and all too readily perhaps, that his silly, strutting fowl cost him cash for every day of their conceited lives.

By the term "fancier," I am obviously not referring to the man who owns a broiler factory or a multi-storied egg plant stocked with one of the common, production-line breeds of fowl. There is no more similarity between a fancier and a poultryman than there is between a philatelist and a postmaster. And a commercial poultryman, should he ever condescend to waste his time looking at our exhibits, is often quite caustic. Many have gone so far as to declare that since most of our birds belong to hobbyists rather than to farmers, the poultry show has no longer any right to be included in an agricultural fair at all.

Those who are more tolerant may smile at us in the forgiving way the world smiles at a poet or an artist. As one of them asked me only recently, "But if you just want something to look at wouldn't canaries be cheaper? And canaries sing!"

What no one seems to suspect is that a fancier is merely a man who is pleasantly haunted by memories of a boyhood spent on a farm or in a small town which he has never really consented to leave regardless of what success he may have attained elsewhere. It may simply be that you cannot forget the kind of chickens your mother used to keep in the pen behind the hollyhocks back home some fifty years ago. Or you remember the comical Leghorn cockerel which you had trained to fly to your bedroom window for corn every morning. Or the Christmas-like thrill of waking to a Fair Day morning in that long ago, knowing that this was at last the great day that you were going to show some of your very own Minorcas, hatched in your own incubator, and from a setting you had bought with your own cash. And if you won first prize, the fifty cents was yours to spend in any way you wanted. Or if the fever had already worked itself deep enough in the blood, you could hide it away until next spring when you could buy another setting of another kind perhaps.

What no one seems to suspect, in short, is that there are more stories in a poultry show than there are breeds.

I met my breed forty years ago in company with a half dozen more of my father's brood one winter's night as we fought for the close places beside his stoveside rocker when the chores and the homework were done. We met it in a tattered old poultry book which my father, in his constant search for economical reading material, had picked up one day at a library sale. The Golden Penciled Hamburgs were on one of the color plates which hadn't fallen out yet.

We had never seen such a bird in the flesh, though our famous Brown Leghorn Prunejuice was indeed so beautiful we still remembered the shine of him. I think, in fact, that in all of the years we looked at that book and talked about these wonderful chickens, they were no more real to us than King Arthur's Knights, or Cinderella, or the Ugly Duckling, or Andersen's fairies—or any of the other enchanted creatures which we used to read about in that lovely hour before we were bundled off to our straw ticks back on the farm.

There were other pictures in that book too, pictures of poultry in a hundred different colors and shapes, poultry with feathered boots, with hats, with yard-long tails, with double combs, extra toes, stilt legs, spurs. But right from the first, the Golden Penciled Hamburgs were our breed— ours because they were our father's choice.

"Now there's a bird that's got some right to holler at the sunrise," he used to say. "If they're as good as their pictures, that is."

And one day when the picture at last fell all the way out of the book, he took our Uncle Bertram's Boer War picture out of its frame and put the Golden Penciled Hamburgs in its place. "I think we're going to have some of those someday," he said

And I remembered how we begged to know if he really meant it. "Really, Daddy? Really for true?"

"Really for true," he promised.

Our mother couldn't understand such adolescence in her husband at all. He was generally so cautious, so solid; and here he was now getting all excited about some fowl that looked more like red and gold pheasants than an honest-to-goodness hen. Chickens like that were all right for rich men to play with, she admitted, but if they were of any use on a farm, they would have been there long ago.

Father didn't argue, which meant that his mind was set. But Mother refused to let the matter drop. "Anyhow," she comforted herself, "you'll never get around to it. It's just one more of those ideas you're always getting out of your dream books!"

Which was almost the truth. Out of the few ragged books which we possessed then had come a lot of dreaming that never did get down to earth. With the help of one such book we once designed a barn. A huge and beautiful thing it was, and equipped with all that was modern. We even picked out the stock to fill it. Our cattle were Galloways and Jerseys. We had a place for two teams of horses. Gray Percherons. And in the sheep shed attached to the south side were a hundred head of Dorsets. I have forgotten now what breed of swine we decided upon, but I know for certain that every animal in that fabulous barn was registered, and as fine as the combined hands of God and man could make it.

It would have been a great misfortune had we ever made a start on the barn. It was much too perfect to run the risk of reality.

The one small part of that marvelous dream which did materialize was the famous Golden Penciled Hamburgs. Not at first, of course, for we must have looked at that picture for all of three years before we got them. There came a fall, however, when our inventory looked so good that Father decided that he might be able to afford a trip down to the Winter Fair. If he could get a ride down on a cattle truck, that is.

When he came back, he brought a pair of the exquisitely barred feathers to show us that he had at last made the face-to-face acquaintance of the breed that had been ours for so long.

"And are they really pretty, Daddy?" we asked. "Really for true?"

"Prettier than the picture," he said. "A lot prettier. You'll see."

The five dozen eggs came one March day when the first warmth of spring was sucking the snow away from the hillsides. I can remember the excitement there was when we unpacked them and found that only two were broken. I remember too how gloomily Mother wondered about their cost. "Probably spent a dollar or more a dozen for those silly eggs," she said. "And him with the seams of his Sunday shoes all gaping open."

I doubt if she ever knew that Father had paid five times that for the eggs. The valuation was on the express label that he doubled up and told me to put in the stove.

So our start in the Hamburgs cost us twenty-five dollars plus the express, plus the secondhand incubator Father bought to bring them to life.

The incubator went into the parlor, which to us children, at least, seemed the only place in the house worthy of it, not only because of the wonderful treasure it held, but because there was an atmosphere of hushed sanctity about our parlor back home that was somehow in keeping with the spirit in which a child, in his eternal quest for something younger than himself, could properly approach the miracle of creation which unfolded behind its glass doors.

Every night for three weeks we made a pilgrimage into the parlor to watch our father test and turn the golden eggs. We went in tiptoeing carefully along the pathway of papers Mother had laid down to protect the carpet, and I recall that when we knelt to look, for some reason or other we always found ourselves speaking in whispers.

Came the twenty-first day when we knelt by the hour to see the humble miracle of life breaking forth from the dead-rock stillness of the egg and becoming the unspeakably beautiful thing which is a chick in its first fluff.

Surely there was never any happening of all those wonderful years more wonderful than those forty-two chicks which stepped out of their shells that spring. And by September, when their plumage was coming into its first full grandeur, they were the pride of the farm.

One of the things I remember clearest is how they would follow Father from one end of the barnyard to the other, coaxing for the bit of corn he always had in his pocket. And how he used to lure them out onto the lawn on a sunny Sunday morning for Father Kelly to see, because their gold and red looked so rich against the green. And to the visitors who were forever coming home from church with us, he'd say quietly, "They're real show stuff, you know. Got the eggs from a man named Humphries. He's supposed to have the best flock in America. . . . Does he make a living out of them? . . . Well no, as a matter of fact he's connected with some sort of steel company. Never saw him, mind you, but I hear he's one of the vice-presidents."

The usual comment might go like this. "Um-hmm. . . . Not a bad-looking sort of bird, Henry. That is if you don't mind a funny color and a flighty sort. . . . Must lay a pretty small egg though, eh, Henry? . . . Wouldn't dress out much either. Or are they one of them new kinds you're supposed to kill young for fryers? . . . Well, they might pan out all right, you know, but me, well, I always did swear by the good old Barred Rocks, you know. . . ."

It got embarrassing after a while when he discovered how hard it was to explain to such neighbors that there were actually breeds of fowl whose greatest purpose was simply to march in the sun and be beautiful. So after a while he would merely say, "Well now, they lay pretty good, you know. Maybe not quite like a Leghorn, but pretty good. And they don't take too much feed."

But he was always careful not to risk such a reply when Mother could hear, for she would interrupt him promptly in the name of honesty and proclaim the fact that his beloved breed was about as much use on a farm as a cage full of monkeys.

He never got much appreciation around home. That which eventually did reach him came from men he had never seen before. First came Mr. Humphries himself. He drove up through the mud of our lane one bleak November in a Packard, and the fineness of him was enough to set us children gawking at him from the safety of the summer kitchen doorway. "Did you have any luck with those eggs you got from me?" he asked.

Father looked doubtfully at the glint on Mr. Humphries' shoes and his low rubbers and then led off through the slop of the barnyard to the henhouse. Mr. Humphries looked at the birds for a long time. "Pure beginner's luck," he said. "I believe you've got almost as good a flock as I have."

Which, so he told us confidentially a little later, was probably the best flock in the whole world.

"But you'll have to send some of these birds down to the

Winter Fair," he said. And without waiting for an answer, he picked out the ones good enough to go and put some colored rings on their legs.

Much to Mother's fright, Mr. Humphries accepted her invitation to supper that night, and she frantically contrived her best for him. Mr. Humphries noticed neither the special food nor the special tablecloth. He just talked Golden Penciled Hamburgs.

"It's knowing how to make the right matings that gives you birds like I've got," he said. "You've got to make one mating for your hens and another to give you your best cock birds. . . . As soon as I get back to the office I'm going to send you a book about that. But you've got to go to the fairs, you know. That's where you really learn."

So Father started going to the shows, his birds often going down to the city in the same cattle truck that took him. And now, in the great bragging sessions that often filled our noon hours at the old school, we finally had something to say about our little father. Before this, he had always been too small, too quiet. We could never hope to brag, as the O'Hara boys could, for instance, that he could lick the next best man in the section with one hand tied down. We knew that he would never own a two-ton team of Belgians, such as Burney MacKillop's dad took to the gravel pit every morning. He had never been overseas, or out west, or in any other of the far countries from which a man ordinarily returns as an everlasting hero.

But our father was famous anyhow. More famous by far than all the rest, we thought. Our dad had some of the best Golden Penciled Hamburgs in the whole wide world. Really, he had. Really for true. Cross our hearts and spit.

Two years later, when Mr. Humphries suddenly died,

and his flock disappeared with him, our Hamburgs were the best anywhere and we soon had a bushel of ribbons to prove it. Even Mother became at least mildly enthusiastic because the ribbons were awfully nice things to make cushions out of.

But as for me, the most swelling pride of all came from seeing the kind of men who used to come down the aisles of the great shows and greet Father as if he were a long-lost brother. A few of these were farmers like himself, but many of them were men with names which you were sure you had heard before—big men in industry, in the world of sports, clergymen, lawyers, men whom you felt must surely be addressed as "sir" back in their paneled offices. But when they were talking exhibition fowl, first names were plenty good enough. Especially if they happened to be among the few who bred Golden Penciled Hamburgs.

"Henry, you old fox!" I can hear them saying. "You've done it again! Took every good ribbon in the class! When are you going to give us other guys a chance?"

"Gave you the pick of the crop last October," Father might remind them.

"But you still beat us! How do you do it?"

And Father would laugh in his shy way and maybe compose a yarn for them. He fed his birds banana centers. Or he kept them by the parlor stove all winter with the Christmas tree for a roost. And come show time, he used the right kind of lipstick to put on their combs.

It got so there was no use telling the boys back at school just how famous he really was. They wouldn't believe. Even when a guy's little brother backed you up and said, "Really for true!"

Their fathers were just as hard to convince, and to them these Gold Hamburgers our father was so insane about were still a funny-colored, crow-meated little bird that wouldn't lay any more eggs than any other kind. And the only thing gold about them was the money Father had had to pay for them.

The years didn't bring Father much of the ease that should have come from his toil and endless saving. Each spring there was the blossoming of new promise, but each summer saw the old, old struggle against the soured and brittle fields and the unconcern of disastrous skies. Always, always there was too little time for all that had to be done, and always there was too little to work with. The logs we had hoarded so carefully to put a new backbone into our sagging barn went to pay the taxes. The family kept growing and so did the bills.

Then electricity came out our way and Father hadn't the heart to ask Mother to wait any longer for its miracle even though he couldn't really afford it.

The only luxury I can ever remember Father allowing himself was that flock of ornamental chickens. And I shall always be able to see him as he would come in some noon from the summer fields, the grime wrinkled in his forehead, his face weary with sun and fatigue, sitting by the well for a moment with his famous chickens gathering around his feet. I can still hear Mother wondering fretfully how long it was going to take "to get you in to dinner."

"The sun and those Hamburgs must have been made on the same day," he used to say.

I was eighteen the year I went to Normal School. That was back in 1932. Oats were bringing a cent a pound that year and we decided we'd feed ours into pork. From the pig money was to come enough to start me off on my great adventure. But when starting time came in September, pigs were bringing so little it was hardly worth a man's effort to load them into the truck. Father decided to hold onto his for a while.

So he gave me what money he had and one memorable day I packed our fiber suitcase and boarded the bus for the city. "I'll send you the rest as soon as I sell the pigs," he promised.

But the price of pigs was to go lower still. Farmers began shooting their piglets at birth that year, because they were worse than worthless.

It wasn't until I hitchhiked home for Thanksgiving that I learned where the money had come from. Father had sold the Golden Penciled Hamburgs.

"Three hundred dollars is a lot of money, son," he explained quietly. "And maybe it was like Mother said anyhow. . . . They always were a sort of a plaything. . . ."

When he saw how badly I felt about it, he tried to joke then. "Guess I showed some of these practical Thomases around here that there was gold in them after all," he said.

That was the day I made a solemn promise to myself that someday, just as soon as ever I could, I'd see to it that the Golden Penciled Hamburgs would come back to my father's farm. It was the only way I could get that Thanksgiving dinner past the lump in my throat.

It was a harder promise to keep than I had anticipated. There was hardly as much money in teaching those depression years as there was in feeding pork. Came then such things as marriage, and then a war. And by the time when I might have bought some of our breed back again, the family had begun to break apart. And Father had moved to the city where chickens are unsanitary, and a rooster is forbidden by law to crow at the morning.

So I was never able to keep that promise, really. But I did buy back some of the Golden Penciled Hamburgs. I got an even dozen of them a few months ago. Not from the man who gave my father $300 for them so long ago, because he died last year. But the son to whom the birds were left was quite pleased to have me take the foolish things off his hands.

And I got a lovely redwood incubator along with them. It's in my front room now beside the television set and my own younger ones have been begging me to load it with eggs ever since we set it up.

The chickens themselves aren't quite as good as they used to be when we had them before. At least that's what Father says. Which is why he's up at my place so much of the time right now.

"It's knowing how to make the right matings that gives you the good birds," he reminds me, and he doesn't think that knowing is quite mine yet.

Come showtime again and the best may once more be ours. But I'm getting a little ahead of my story now.

Chapter 14

I T W O U L D H A R D L Y be honest for me to leave the impression that our father was always gentle and patient with his family. He could, if the occasion warranted, shiver us with a rather surprising anger; and this was particularly so if one of us children should insist upon adding to his burdens when he was already shouldering as much as he could carry.

There was, for instance, that awful day when Father declared that he was going to give my brother Eddie a licking. A whipping in itself was not exactly a rarity at our place, but it was rare indeed to see Father determined to administer a "scutching" while he was still angry. Generally he managed to postpone the grim event until the air had cooled a little. It was easier then to decide just how deserving the rascal in question might be.

But it wasn't that way the day he cut the switch for my brother Eddie. He was so full of wrath that day that he frightened us all, I think.

We came up from the oat field at eleven that morning. Father's face was tight and the wheels of our grain wagon spun angrily in the dust of the lane. The first frantic day of harvest had scarcely begun and our binder had broken down. Not that it was such a serious break, but we just hadn't the *time* for it. Time was pure gold right now!

Father glanced at the slowly thickening sky to the west and strode across the barnyard to the workshop he kept in the corner of the feedroom, and he kept repeating the things he would have to take back to the field with him: "Hammer, wrench, saw, brace and bit . . . for Petesakes, don't forget anything now! . . ." he warned himself.

The comfortable sound of grunting within cut his thinking short, and when he threw open the feedroom door, the rush of startled pigs through his legs very nearly upended him. The floor was ankle deep in feed. Two bags of chop had been completely emptied and two more had been sampled. A window, which he had leaned in one corner to wait for winter, had been splintered into a thousand pieces and thoroughly mixed into the rest of the mess. And on the workbench there was hardly a tool to be found. No hammer, no wrench, no saw, no brace and bit.

"That boy! That boy!" Father shut his eyes so tight they must have hurt and clenched his fists. "I could skin him alive!" he cried.

He went outside again and looked over toward the house. Two of the youngest were playing in the sand behind the cistern but there was no Eddie. "Nine years old is enough for a lad to learn some responsibility," Father announced significantly. "I learned it long before then."

He went over to the orchard, selected a maroon-colored apple switch and then went into the kitchen. Mother saw the switch and looked up from her washing. "It's time that

Eddie had a little lumber laid on him, I think," Father explained. And he told her what had happened to the feedroom. "A little lumber laid on the right place and maybe the next time he swipes my tools he'll remember to at least close the door behind him." His voice was still high with anger.

Mother said she didn't know exactly where Eddie was but she knew he had been getting his soapbox racer fixed up to take over to the Kelsoes. They were going to race on the hill over there. That's why he had got the tools, no doubt.

Then she stopped and looked at Father with the look she always gave him when she wanted to change his mind. "He didn't mean anything," she said quietly. And at that moment she caught sight of the missing tools on top of the old cupboard on the back porch. "You see," she said, pointing them out, "he intended to put them back. . . . You wouldn't really thrash him, would you, Henry?"

And she smiled as if to say that she knew very well that he wouldn't.

But it was different this time. "When Eddie comes home," he said firmly, "I'm going to commence his more serious education. And when I'm done with him, maybe he'll take time out to *think* a little." Then, as if to justify his indignation, he gave us all a little lecture as we sat at dinner.

"That's the trouble with kids nowadays! They just don't think! Now when I was Eddie's age I milked three cows, cut all the stovewood and pitched sheaves when there were sheaves to be pitched. Not that I'm wishing a tough life like that on any progeny of mine, but, blast it all, is it too much to ask them to think?"

Eddie wasn't at that dinner of course. He was still over at Kelso's hill, Mother thought, but he ought to be home soon.

"He ought to be home *now*," Father said, and he said it in a voice that made the cat blink. "That feed's worth three dollars a sack and there's so much glass in it now I'll have to bury it!"

The younger ones began looking at their mother over half-finished plates and the baby in the highchair had the beginning of a pucker in his underlip. "If he doesn't soon come, I'll call the Kelsoes," Mother said as she kept shoving her choicest victuals down to Father's end of the table.

Eddie didn't come. Father got up from his plate and went through the morning's mail. Nothing but ads for things that he needed and couldn't afford to buy and bills for things he had needed and couldn't afford and had bought anyhow.

It was when Father was out on the back steps looking at the slightly ominous sky above the swamp that he noticed that peculiar combination of two-by-fours, orange crates and cast-off wheels known to Eddie's gang as a "soapbox car." The sight of it troubled him more than he cared to admit.

"Jean," he said, coming back to the door, "Eddie can't be coasting at Kelso's at all. His car's down by the silo."

The spoon of porridge in Mother's hand stopped half-way to the baby's mouth. "I'll phone," she said.

No, Eddie wasn't at Kelso's. The boys said he had promised to come over this morning but he hadn't showed up. Would he be back of old lady McBride's maybe? Down at the swimming pool?

We called Mrs. McBride. No, Mrs. McBride hadn't

seen anyone go back that way this morning. He might be there, of course, but she didn't think so. Had we called the Bolens?

Mother called the Bolens. Then she called the Henniseys, the MacDonalds, the Dunns, the Heffernans, the Kavanaughs. She called the people who lived next the schoolgrounds. Nobody had seen him.

"That boy! That boy!" Father muttered, but still with more irritation in the words than alarm. There was no use getting excited, really. A boy that age could look after himself.

But Mother folded limply into a nearby chair. The baby began to cry. "You better phone," she said.

"Now, Jean," he comforted, "let's keep the hysterics out of it. Why, I remember once at home we got the whole neighborhood excited about one of the kids evaporating and we finally found him sleeping in the barn. How be you take a look upstairs and I'll tour outside."

So they searched. They searched everywhere they could think of, even in places where they could be absolutely certain that he couldn't be. They called.

And now the ragged edge of panic was biting into Father too in spite of his fight to keep it away. He went to the phone and cranked the long, shrill ring which everyone would recognize as the signal for an emergency.

No, nobody on the line had seen Eddie. Should they come down and help look?

Not yet, Father told them, still trying stubbornly to convince himself and the rest of us that there was nothing to worry about. He sat down and noticed that Mother's eyes were full. "Look here," he said, "there's just got to be a clue somewhere, Jean. When did you last see him? What was he doing? Has he been coaxing to go any place lately?"

Mother did her best to level out her thinking. "Day before yesterday," she said, "he was coaxing to go back to the swamp for a baby crow. But you knew about that."

Yes, Father knew about that all right because Eddie had spent half of the morning trailing him around the farm and begging for permission. Father had told him no. There were too many non-profit animals on the place already and it was too late in the year to get a crow in the nest anyhow.

But Eddie had insisted that he knew of a tree where the crows always gathered at night to feed their young and he knew a way to build a trap that would catch one.

"That trap he built!" Father said suddenly getting excited. "That crazy crow trap he made out of wire netting! Where did he put that?"

Mother thought that he kept it under the cellar steps along with the rest of the junk that she wouldn't allow into his bedroom. We went to look.

If it's gone, Father told us, we'll have the answer.

But the trap wasn't gone.

After a while we all began thinking of that swimming pool behind old lady McBride's place. Father didn't like to think of that and he mustered all of the arguments he could to tell himself that the boy couldn't be there, but in the end he said, "Maybe you'd call Mrs. Gillen to come over and stay with you, Jean. I'm going back along the creek to have a look. If I don't find any trace of him right away, we'll ask for help. . . ."

The creek angled across the back of our farm but the pool that the boys used for swimming was downstream near the road, just back of Mrs. McBride's. Generally the boys went by the road, but one could, of course, go through the fields. Maybe Eddie had done that and Mrs.

McBride hadn't seen him. There just had to be a clue somewhere!

He found the first clue in the track in the creek bank. The track was fresh and there was no mistaking the tread of Eddie's new canvas shoes. More heartening still was the fact that it didn't lead down toward the swimming pool at all. It climbed the opposite bank and headed out toward the swamp.

"He went out after a crow after all!" Father exclaimed aloud, and headed on the run for his tractor. "Now what the sam hill would make him so blasted emptyheaded as to take off like that without telling someone!"

He headed his tractor across the fields and toward the swamp on the gallop, and in his quivering mind, he already had the boy squirming in his grasp. "I'll tack his hide to the barn door!" he thought. "Crows! What the sam hill's the almighty attraction in crows anyhow?"

We knew exactly where the famous crow tree stood. Eddie had pointed it out many a time and begged his father to go back there with him to explore the nests which were always clogging up the higher branches. It was a big pine tree which stood on a little knoll just inside the rim of alders at the swamp's border.

But Eddie wasn't at the crow tree. It didn't even look as though he had ever been there, because there seemed to be no tracks at all in the soft earth which fell away from the knoll on all sides. We called and called to make sure, but there was no answer. There wasn't even a crow to notice it because they were all away for the day.

So we rode the tractor back home again, back along the lovely, lovely field of oats that Father had so desperately wanted to reap before the weather had time to play hob with it.

Mrs. Gillen was in the kitchen with Mother when he got to the house. Mrs. Gillen was a motherly sort, with quiet competence stamped in every line of her face, but it was easy to see that, for all her comfort, Mother was getting nearer the breaking point.

Mrs. Gillen said, "I've just been telling your wife that Mr. Goldbloom is offering ten cents a pound for wild raspberries. Don't you think Eddie might be off picking somewhere?"

Father looked beneath the sink for the two big honey pails which they always used for picking. They were gone. "I think he's been making sandwiches too," Mother said, brightening. "Somebody's been into the bread."

All right, Father told us. Now we know for sure. He went back to the swamp but he didn't go for crows. He went for raspberries. But why isn't he back? And why didn't he tell somebody?

He looked at the clock. Quarter past one. As near as anyone could guess, Eddie had been away about four hours now. Any way you figure it out, he should have been back.

"I'm going back to the swamp to have a look," Father said. "And, Mrs. Gillen, maybe you'd find out whether there are any of the neighbors that would like to give me a hand?"

"Shouldn't I call the police?"

Father thought it over. He had always hated to be the center of a big scene. And the boy couldn't be too far away. They'd find him sleeping somewhere in the shade and then there would be the whole crowd of the curious to laugh at him maybe. "Just get me a few neighbors. We know the country better than the police anyhow."

So he started the long search alone. He tried to guess what route his son would have chosen, and where the

imaginary trail came to the rim of the swamp, he exam-
ined the earth with infinite patience. After a while he
thought he found the place. The ground was a bit too dry
here to hold a print, but there was a place where the dry
grass and the mullein had obviously been trampled. A calf
or a stray dog might have done that, of course, but Father
didn't think so, and he followed the uncertain trail as far
into the swamp as he could follow it.

When he could follow no longer, he headed for the open
space where, in years gone by, the family had always gone
to pick raspberries. He looked at the bushes closely. Surely
enough, somebody had been picking. There were broken
and bent canes too.

"He's been here all right!" he said. "I'm on the right
track!"

Then he called. He called till he was hoarse, but each
time his frantic voice filtered away through the dense
alders and birch with no more answer to it than the jays
and the crickets could give. He followed the berry canes
deeper and deeper into the swamp. The ground got soft
now and he began looking again for the print of that
canvas shoe.

"He's been here!" he kept telling himself. "I know he's
been here! What else would have left those berry bushes
looking like that?"

Which was a question he shouldn't have asked himself,
because he couldn't help thinking that a bear might have
made them look like that. Or was a bear too big now? Sure
it was too big. A bear would have left a trail a yard wide. If
the marks had been made by any animal at all it must have
been a coon. But he wasn't sure enough about that and so
he began to pray about it. "Lord," he said, "it isn't right

for a helpless kid to be alone in a place like this. Let me find him!"

The going got tougher as he stumbled on. The vines and burrs snatched at his legs and the birches slapped at his face. It was hot. There wasn't the slightest trace of breeze. Pools of muck soup hid under dead fern clumps, and once he lost his shoe in one. The black flies and mosquitoes, thank God, weren't as bad today as they generally were. It was too hot and too dry for them perhaps, but they were bad enough to bring the blood to Father's surface in a half dozen places that first hour he was in the swamp.

Once, when he called, he was sure he heard an answer, and the delight of it swelled his throat so tight that he could hardly give the call over again. The only thing wrong with the answer was that it seemed to come from behind, from the direction he had just come.

It did. It was the call of the first of the neighbors which Mrs. Gillen had sent to the rescue. I was with them.

We hunted all of that afternoon. We hunted first in the haphazard fashion of a bunch of hounds and then some of the wiser men called us all together and formed us into a rank. Then we started the search all over again, each keeping within sight of the one next him, and the whole line moving slowly toward the heart of the swamp.

There were stops. There were more bent berry canes to examine. There were more tracks, but whether they were those of a lost boy or of our own foolish making, we could not decide. And then someone found the waxed bread wrapper and the tiniest piece of crust. The crust was fresh. Eddie had been that way.

It was Joe Friday, the drain commissioner, who first

sobered the rejoicing that took hold of the crowd when they found that.

"A lad's that's this far in is pretty badly lost," he said.

So someone went back to the house and phoned the police then, and an hour or so later, all the women on the side road got together and set up a soup kettle and a cream can of water at the edge of the swamp. By dark that night, they were bringing in everything from fried chicken to doughnuts. It was the women who gathered up all of the lanterns and flashlights too, because the search mustn't stop for an instant.

Night brought the mosquitoes out of the damp grass, and the torture of them was enough to make some of the men send their wives home for concoctions to keep the pests at a distance. It was going to be a long, long night.

The mosquitoes brought a new worry to Father— Not for himself or the men in the search, but for Eddie. How long could a lad's tender skin endure the torment of so thick a cloud of them?

One of the older and less tactful of our neighbors said, "I think you might as well face the facts, Henry. If we don't find him before morning, we might never find him."

It was about then that one of the policemen caught up with Father and took him aside. "How old was this boy?" he asked. "What was he wearing? What color is his hair? How high is he?"

Father was surprised that it should be so hard for him to answer. He hadn't the slightest idea what Eddie had been wearing that day. Overalls, he guessed. Overalls and some kind of a shirt. And his hair? Well, it wasn't black. Sort of a khaki color, maybe. Or maybe a dull sort of blond. He couldn't seem to remember. All he could remember was that the very first time he had seen him—meaning the day he had been born—Eddie didn't seem to have had any hair at all. Sure, he had hair now, but Father couldn't for the life of him remember when he had last taken a good look at it. And how high was he? Up to his middle? Oh, more than that now, surely! But why couldn't he remember? He didn't say so, but he was uncomfortably ashamed of himself.

"There's a man up at the Narrows who raises bloodhounds," the policeman was saying. "I have his address here, if you think you'd like to call him. When you can show them a definite starting point, bloodhounds sometimes do a very nice job. Of course it would cost a bit of money to get them down here from that far away."

"Give me the address," Father said. "I'll send a man in to phone right away."

And then Father Kelly came over and put an arm about him. "You better go up to the house yourself, Henry. You've been at this too long already. You look like you're almost ready for a stretcher. Call the bloodhound man and then lay down for an hour or two. Go on now. We can carry on, and your wife needs you."

So someone took Father back to the house and he phoned. Mother, so he noticed thankfully, had fallen into a troubled sleep and he lay down on the couch so he wouldn't disturb her. It was no use. His head throbbed and the sweat from his face made a smudge on the cushion. He got up and went outside. He walked over to the silo and looked for a long time at the crazy soapbox car, at the waste of lumber and nails in it, thought of the tools that had been lost or spoiled in its making, of the junk heap it would make when the fancy would pass. And he bent over, took the contraption by the back and shoved it into the shelter of the drive shed. "It might rain tonight," he thought.

He went down cellar then and stretched out on the floor thinking that the cool of the damp cement would take some of the ache from him. But that was no use either, and after a minute or two he got up and went back to the swamp and the long, tired line of cursing searchers and the treacherous, stabbing birches which were always leaning down through the dark to find your eyes.

"If he had only thought!" Father kept saying. "If he'd just taken the time to think!" But there was really no anger left in him now. Only the silent, stubborn prayer, "Lord, it isn't right! Let me find him!"

A few of the women stayed by the fire and the soup pot all night long, and it was they who saw Eddie first. He came down along the outside rim of the swamp and was in the middle of them before they noticed. He came from the direction of the knoll and the crow tree, just about sunrise. There was so much mud caked on his arms and face that they could hardly recognize him.

When they did, one woman could think of nothing better to do than to scream. Another ran to the Model T truck which had brought the water and laid down on the horn and two more found two more horns. It was Eddie himself who first thought of dipping out some soup.

Father was one of the first of the men to make the open again. He came on the dead run, and then when he saw that it was really Eddie, alive and unhurt, he brought himself up short. "Got to watch this," he told himself. "Got to keep the hysterics out of it!"

So he simply set to work to peel some of the mud from the boy's face. "You feel all right?" he asked.

Eddie had decided that he didn't want the soup after all.

Now that his dad was with him, he wanted to cry. "Yes," he sobbed, "I'm all right."

"Why all this mud?" Father asked, trying to get the lad's mind on something better.

"Because the mosquitoes don't bite through it. Not if you put it on thick enough."

Well, Father thought, he sure used his head there. "And how did you find your way back, Eddie?"

Eddie said it wasn't very hard at all after he had figured out the right way. He just remembered that every night and every morning the crows gathered at the big pine on the knoll. He had watched which way they flew last night and started to follow. But he hadn't been able to finish the distance till after it got light this morning.

"Longheadedest lad I ever heard of," Father Kelly said. "Where's he get all that genius anyhow, Henry?"

It was when they were loading Eddie up in the police car that Father noticed the honey pails. They were full. "So you *were* picking berries after all?" he asked.

But for some reason Eddie began to cry again and we never got the answer until we had gone through the jubilation of a second reunion at the house. Indeed it wasn't until Mother was tearfully helping her boy into some fresh clothes that we got the full story. "I forgot the feedroom door again," he said to Father. "The pigs got in and spoiled a lot of feed on you. I was going to get some berries to help pay for it, that's all."

Another day's mail had arrived by the time we were fed again and over our tears; and Father saw that there were two more bills in it. Mrs. Gillen told him too that the bloodhound man had just arrived at the station, and he realized that that would cost him a penny too even though he had no use for the man now. And when he looked out over the swamp, he saw the first forks of a coming storm. It looked bad out there, looked as if there might be wind or hail, or both in those clouds. But he felt as though he hadn't a care in the world now.

How high was the lad? So high that the top of his head came even with his heart. He could still feel the place. And the color of his hair. Well, there was no word really for that color, but Father would remember the exact shade of it now as long as he lived. And he would never forget the smell of the sun and the marsh grass and the wild raspberries in it either.

Chapter 15

ONE DAY LAST June as I was driving through this other town which has now become home to me, I was astounded to hear the unmistakable cawing of a young crow within a stone's throw of the main street. For a moment I wondered if the magic of spring might not be affecting the crows as it does our teen-age lovebirds, making them too bold sometimes for their own good. And then I suddenly realized the truth. This was a pet crow. I knew that by the peculiar uneven tenor of his voice—as if his crop was full of sand—and the impatient way he was begging for food and attention.

Immediately I felt a nostalgic tinge of envy for the boy who owned that crow, for a long time ago—forty-odd years or more—I too came back from high adventure in a swamp one day with a squalling, lousy, doubtful-smelling crow tucked under my arm. And in those hectic weeks that followed I also knew the never-ending battle to find more worms for that bottomless noisy red mouth. More! More! More! And I had to fight off the bloodthirsty ambitions of practical-minded neighbors and itchy-fingered hunters who seemed to think that the coddling of such vermin was a mortal sin.

For the memorable adventure of possessing a pet crow doesn't end with the thrill of climbing an impossible tree to the nest and warding off the ferocity of the older crows while the capture is made. Nor is it over when you have convinced the family and sundry other traditionalists that your crow is to be left alone. For me, the most unforgettable part of my adventure with our pet crow was the discovery of a delightful and endlessly amazing personality. Because in spite of the fact that Jim was forever begging food and attention, he was as rugged an individualist as ever was mentioned in any American schoolbook. In addition, he had the eye of an eagle, the caprice of a little girl and the mischievous imagination of Peck's bad boy.

Nothing on the farm was too small or too insignificant for his minute attention. He sat in the stable aisle while we milked, followed us to the hay fields and to the stooking, inspected every garden row we had to hoe and eventually learned that hunting potato bugs was an excellent sport for himself and an appetizing source of protein as well.

And if the fickle humans on the farm were too tired to talk to him, or our mother had hurt his feelings with an indignant broom, Jim would fly out to the pasture where he would land on the old bay mare and ride horseback all afternoon.

The commencement of school was also a mystery which Jim had to solve, and one morning he followed us the mile or so across town to school where he immediately lightened the day's dreary education by flying right through the window and onto my brother's desk, where he promptly became interested in the ink well.

Indeed the adventures which Jim survived in that year he was a member of our household would make a book in themselves. And that book would perhaps explain our age's newfound urge to make the acquaintance of pets which money cannot buy and for which no book of directions has yet been published. But books about off-trail pets themselves are legion.

Surely it is no mere coincidence that it has suddenly become so profitable for a writer to describe his adventures and friendships with animals which we scarcely even knew before. What is the reason then? Have we suddenly grown tired of our dogs and cats?

We have had our dogs for a long time. They probably shared the first caves with us. But in all this long association we have loved our dogs in much the same way as an important wife loves a husband she can wrap around her finger whenever she isn't snapping it at him. We have tolerated the dog down through the centuries because we were flattered by his undying devotion and his adulation.

It hasn't been quite the same with cats, of course. If a cat has any personality at all he prefers to keep it to himself. Instead he merely squats comfortably in your favorite chair and glumly studies the humans he has condescended to live with.

But now we are becoming intensely intrigued by pets which neither grovel at our feet nor look at us contemptuously from a pinnacle of high disdain. We are discovering as never before the unbelievable fascination of animals which consider themselves lords of creation just the same as we do: animals we can never hope to master; animals which will never be converted to the theology that man is only a little lower than the angels. It is significant that in the many books now describing the fascination of such pets, none of the animals has been caged or conquered. Gavin Maxwell's otters come and go along the Scottish coast as free as a pair of bachelors. Peter Krott's wolverines are also incurably happy wanderers. The door in Rowena Farr's cottage is always left purposely ajar so that her seal can go out for his morning swim without asking anybody. And to Joy Adamson freedom is such an important theme that it is the key word of her best titles.

Surely there is something heartening about the fact that at long last mankind seems to be willing to include animals too in his noble idea of democracy and equal rights for all. Who knows but what the time may come when we may even extend the list to include Chinese and West Indians and even Canadians who speak with an accent.

In this craze to coexist with other forms of animal life, we were merely forty years too modern in my father's house, for we had dozens of such pets.

But to get back to my crow, Jim. I must admit that his sins were even more endearing than either his genius or his virtues. The most disastrously incurable feature of my crow was the fact that he could not resist the fascination of glitter. Everything which was bright shone like a little Grail to him. And if it were small enough to carry, Jim would fly away with it to a place where he could investigate his trophy in privacy. And since our old vine-covered outhouse was the most private place on the farm, we often witnessed the spectacle of an angry young sister crawling about those private premises on her hands and knees, sobbing her heart out as she searched through the luxuriant grass for a missing necklace or ring.

And one Sunday morning when it was Mother's turn to

go hunting for her one and only brooch, Jim came so perilously near to execution that only the sanctity of the Sabbath saved him. But two days later when Mother was still vowing vengeance, one of my smoking uncles happened to leave his plug of Big Ben on the shelf outside the summer kitchen door. (That was as far as it dared to come, for Mother never allowed smoking in our house, even for uncles!)

Now if you are old enough to remember the good old days you will recall that smoking tobacco of the whittling kind used to have a little tin heart with the brand name stuck into the middle of each plug. It was this which Jim's eagle eye spotted at once and he immediately spirited the strange booty away to his favorite private place.

But this time, for reasons known only to himself, Jim went inside the building to make his examination, and when he finally came out he had only the little tin heart in his beak. The rest had been dropped exactly where Mother thought all tobacco ought to go. And Jim and Mother seemed to understand each other very well after that.

I have already hinted, however, that Jim was only one in a long list of creatures which, at some time or other, were part of the noisy, throbbing life at the Green farm. There were the cocoons, for instance, which were discovered in the most unlikely places every fall, caged in a bottle a quarter full of earth, and then left with the geraniums on the window sill in hope of a little resurrection. There was the glass cage of frogs, the crickets in the woodbox, the goldfish which had to share their bowl with the minnows and rainbow darters we found in our creek. We will always remember too the fat, spoiled coons which used to love us one moment and swear at us the next; the snakes we kept to prove that we had conquered fear; the dear old groundhog which was so loving that it used to sleep in the rocking chair till Father made the mistake one day of sitting on it.

Most of the undomesticated creatures which were introduced to our way of life in those days came in spite of our mother's bewildered protests; and Father, nature lover that he was, frequently tried to take her side. In may seem strange then that our crayfish—the least attractive, least lovable of all the animals we claimed as pets—should have been such a lifelong favorite of Father's. I can never recall a winter that we didn't have a collection of those lowly little beasts in our house. Generally the crayfish were kept in a long square roasting pan near the stovepipe in the boys' room. Such a pan was filled half with water and half with a bank of sandy clay, and a piece of screening across the top kept our curious guests where we wanted them. We used to find bright stones to put in the water end of the pan, and at night after the house was quiet we could often hear them crawling after their huge and murderous-looking claws, or rattling their prehistoric armor against the tin of their tank.

They were stupid, cement-colored, outlandish-looking animals really, and no one seemed to have any affection for them but ourselves. We loved to watch them burrow into the sand, and when company called after church on Sundays, we would take the crayfish out and let them hang on our fingers with their pincers to show off.

In the summer evenings hunting them in the creek was always a delightful sport. It was so much more fun than fishing. It took more skill, and there was the joy of pursuit as well as surprise.

"Look!" my father would say as we would wade into the shallow water around their rocks. "Look! There goes a whopper! Here, let me take the big sieve." Then to the crayfish, "You're a brave fellow, aren't you? You are brave and you are wise. Wise enough to retreat before someone too strong for you, and yet you are brave enough to retreat with your face to the foe."

And this peculiar trait of always swimming backwards and with his face to the foe was used to capture the crayfish, for while one of our party attracted his attention and advanced upon him slowly from the front, another would sneak up behind with Mother's sieve and let the unwary creature back into it.

We fished in order to furnish food for the table, and for that reason fishing was scarcely a sport to us. But crayfish hunting was pure pleasure and nothing else. And when we saw them through our father's eyes, crayfish were such remarkable little fellows!

"See here, boys," Father would say, holding a fat one behind the claws, "here's an old girl with her young all tucked under her tail! She's no fool! She knows enough not to leave them lying around for the pollywogs to feed on! And she's been in a fight, too! See, she's lost a claw at some time. Sometimes they grab hold of something and they just won't let go. They would sooner lose a claw than to let go and that is just what happens. But that doesn't bother them much, because they just bud out another one in its place. This smaller one here is a new claw. See it, boys?"

And when Father took time out to explain it to us, the humblest work of nature seemed a miracle. But the peculiar fascination which the crayfish had for all of us was due to something more than chasing them under the rocks of our creek, or watching the captured ones in the pan by the bedroom stovepipe.

It came from listening to the delightfully incredible

story which Father used to tell us of the blue crayfish, the story which he told us over and over again because we were never tired of coaxing it out of him.

"When I was eight years old," he would begin looking dreamily into the open stove door, "when I was just as old as Harry here, my father took us way up into Bruce County to clear a piece of land for a rich man. It took us two days to get there, and we traveled in a lumber wagon with four horses. Oh, it was a rare kind of wagon, all right. We had a frame covered with canvas sacking built right on the wagon, and we carried our grub and our pots and pans right with us. Did we sleep out in the open? Sure we did, right beneath the wagon! Why, I think the best fun I ever had was riding with my father in that outfit over those rough trails! . . .

.   .   ,

"And when we finally got there we camped right beside the most beautiful little spring you ever saw. It bubbled right out of the rock, and it trickled over the stones as clear as could be. I was too young to do much work then, and so I used to play around this spring every afternoon dabbling in the water, oh, you know—damming it up and letting it overflow, and all that. And climbing the birches that grew beside it.

"And one afternoon I saw something in that spring that I have never seen since. It was a blue crayfish. It was a real crayfish, mind you, just as big as those we have in the pan, but blue! Man, but it was blue! Blue as the lowside of a rainbow! And with the tips of his claws as orange as a tiger lily. Well, you know when that crayfish slipped off a stone and I could see him in that clear clear water, I thought I had never seen anything so pretty in all my life! I spent all that afternoon trying to catch him and finally I did.

"They are smarter than our own crayfish, seems to me, and they swim faster. But the next day I found two more and the way I figured it they live in little villages, sort of. Looked to me like they even had a king and queen, because it seemed to me that it was always the two biggest ones who came out to face you, and the rest stayed behind hidden in the rocks with just their long antennae and the tips of their orange claws showing.

.   .   .

"Yes, sir, I think that was the best summer I ever had. And you know sometime, when things are a little better and we have a little more money, I think maybe I'm going back and find that same little spring with the blue crayfish, and maybe just stay there a day or two lying around under those birches and watching those blue crayfish flash in the spring. Man, but they were pretty!"

And now he would look again into the depths of the fire, while we children for the moment sat wrapped in the quiet of entrancement.

I do not think we were ever greatly concerned with fairies in our childhood; nor had giants, elves, princes and the seven dwarfs much place in our fanciful mental meanderings. But I think we all built up many a gorgeous fantasy about the little blue creatures in that faraway spring. We pictured their little villages with clay castles and soldiers and kings, and at night as we lay abed we would compare our conceptions of what the blue crayfish must have looked like.

"Are we really going to that spring again sometime, Dad?" we would ask.

"Yes," he would tell us with that sober, dreamlike expression taking hold of him again, "I think that someday we're going to find it again. And we're going to catch some of those crayfish and bring them back with us," he said.

"Now why will you lie like that to these children?" Mother would ask, impatient at such nonsense.

"Someday I *am* going," he would say with calm emphasis, "and I'm going to take any of these children who want to go with me, and we're going in a wagon just like my father had—only better!"

Mother, to put an end to further discussion, would hand Father the Bible storybook to read, and another day would be over. But such reading seemed especially dull after such a promise, and I remember that the younger ones used to take Father by the hand as he walked up the dark cold stairs to bed, and whisper so Mother couldn't hear, "Will you really take us someday? Really?"

But the years gathered behind us, and the memories we thought could never dim floated back out of reach and lost themselves in that sad-bright haze where truth and legend can no longer be kept apart. Pair by pair the fat bow legs of the toddlers straightened, grew fiercely strong and independent. Grunts and cute gibberish gave way to words which set the older ones to laughing; the words mustered into voices which demanded, complained, accused and earned the first spankings; the voices thickened and grew taller. The girls began to giggle and whisper and blush; the big, big boys to defy the whole world.

Still we hadn't made the promised trip. And though it hadn't been forgotten, Mother no longer complained when it was mentioned.

"Henry," she said one winter's night when we were around the stove and the young ones were all climbing over him at once, "Henry, did you really see such an animal as you've been telling these kids all these years?

Were those crayfish blue, blue—like you say they were? Are you sure?"

And Father looked around at her as if she had suddenly announced that she no longer loved him. He wouldn't even answer her.

It was that same year, I think, that I entered high school. It was a rare attainment in those days, and while Father would never have allowed himself to say so, I think that he was prouder of it than I was.

My education was already long past the stage where he could help with my homework, but over my shoulder he followed my lessons as attentively as ever. "But how's this," he asked, "that you just study plants for your science? Don't you pay no attention at all to animals?"

That came next year, I told him, in zoology.

So he waited a year, and then one November when the cold was rapping at the door again, he looked up from my zoology text. "Doesn't seem to be much of anything here about crayfish," he said. "I hear that this new science teacher is a pretty sharp lad though, and I reckon he's probably got a whole bushel of science books at home. How be you ask him sometime if there's such a thing as a blue crayfish? You think he'd mind?"

In due time, when I had found enough courage, I took the question to Mr. Steeves; and the day after, this earnest young man shook his head as he gave me his answer. "I have several books on Amphibia," he said, "but I can't find any mention at all of a blue crayfish."

Then, since we were alone, I explained something of the reason for Father's peculiar question.

"Oh," said Mr. Steeves, "that's interesting! . . . Look,

why don't you let me write an old professor friend of mine? I'm sure he must know the Crustaceans much better than I do. Maybe he'll tell us."

It took several months for the professor's answer to come back, and there was no comfort in it at all. He had never seen a blue crayfish and he could find no mention of one in any of his references.

"Now what did I tell you, Henry?" Mother twitted. And again Father had no reply.

It was the year I graduated that Father Kelly was drawn into the problem. If I remember correctly, Father had invited the priest up to see his famous flock of Golden Penciled Hamburgs. "Come and take a last look at them," he said, "because I'm going to let them go next week."

But as so often happened, the visit didn't end with an inspection of Father's flowers and fancy chickens. That evening as the two men sat by the pump on the back veranda while the sun burned down in the west, Father said, "Now tell me, Kelly, are you still sure? Are you as sure for instance as the folks you preach to?"

Father Kelly thought that over carefully. "If I wasn't *pretty* sure, Henry, I think I'd be honest enough to quit the priesthood."

"But are you as sure now as you were when you were young and everything was new and simple?"

Again Father Kelly was in no hurry to answer. "Ah, to have the unclouded eyes of a child again!" he exclaimed softly. "Ah, for the days when seeing was believing!"

"Me, I was so awful sure back there in those Pepabun camp meetings, Kelly. And—well, I'm still sure, you know. Only it's in a different way now. . . . I guess I don't make sense, do I? . . . What I mean is that I used to tell myself and everybody else: 'I know! I know!' . . . And I'll tell you straight, Kelly, I was so sure that what I believed was the truth the whole truth and nothing but the truth that you could have massacred me for it! But now—well, now I'm forever wondering about everything. Wondering . . . wondering . . . no end to it!"

The priest quietly studied the sun's last cinders. "Somehow I don't figure that our Lord expects you to feel guilty about that, Henry. Maybe it's heresy for me to admit it but it's the kind of faith which has no wonder in it at all which has made all the holy wars. . . . No, Henry, there should be more like you! . . . Ah, what a shame it is that in this age when wonders never cease, we have so quickly ceased to wonder!"

Which were comforting and kindly sentiments indeed and Father said thank you for them. But he observed that wondering, for all its merit, didn't always make a man happy. "By the way, Kelly," Father cut in suddenly, "didn't you tell me that you once had a church up in Bruce County somewheres?"

"That I did," Father Kelly told him. "When I was a young man. And I must say that I loved it up there. So wild and unspoiled, you know."

Father brought his rocker up straight. "Did you by any chance ever see any crayfish up there?"

Father Kelly said that he had indeed. "Many times, in fact. Used to catch pike with them. And I did a lot of fishing up there, you know."

"Were any of them blue? The crayfish, I mean?"

"Blue?" Father Kelly repeated. "Blue? You're talking of these critters that look like little lobsters now, aren't you? . . . Oh no, the only ones I ever saw were the color of mud. . . . What's your reason for asking such a question as that now, Henry?"

But there was now more reason for that question than could be answered by any mere telling of the story which we children knew by heart.

The reason was still restless in him next day when he took me out to the fields to see if the alsike was ready to cut yet. "If I'm ever going to make that trip," he confided, "I guess it better be soon. Here you are off to Normal next fall and dear knows if you'll ever be back to stay, or who'll be the next to leave the nest. And I guess it could never be the trip I've always dreamed of if I didn't have all the kids along. . . . I wonder now if we could get some kind of caravan put together in time to make that trip right after harvest. What do you think?"

My first thought was that since we were now living in the automobile age and our own Model T was perfectly capable, we should simplify everything by planning a motor pilgrimage. But I soon knew better than to press that idea. The dream was too beautifully precise as it was, and to try to change any part of it was like trying to change a man's poetry for him.

So it had to be a wagon trip. Well, what kind of wagon?

One morning that July as we stood knee-deep in the corn rows hoeing and weeding, a caravan of gypsies moved slowly up the road and encamped a half mile away on the commons. Father's eyes followed the gaudy procession with a curious excitement, and that night he did his part of the chores with a careless haste that was most unusual for him, so that he might visit the camp.

"They have a wagon just like we need to go to the spring in," he said excitedly.

And that night as we sat about the gypsies' campfire, I saw that Father was not in the least interested in the horses they wanted to trade, as he was generally, nor did he listen very attentively to the tales these colorful wanderers told about the marvels of the world they had seen. Even the dark old fiddler sitting in the back of the wagon drew little of his attention that night. It was the wagon he loved. I saw his eye taking in every detail of its construction and design. He looked at the gearing, the way the body was slung, the amount of springing needed, the set of the driver's seat and of the windows. He even climbed to the roof to examine the material used in its bracing.

The next morning he set out early for the lumber mill with an assorted load of seasoned logs, and when he came back I noticed that hidden away in the load of finished lumber was a can of red paint and a bag of screwnails. We children knew enough to keep quiet the fact that Dad had dismantled his perfectly good spring wagon, and had in his spare time laid the foundation for his own new caravan. It would have been unfortunate had Mother found out in time.

But we kept our dream ship safely tucked away between the strawstack and the back of the barn where Mother never went, and night after night we planned and worked together until finally the great day came for the unveiling.

We had really done a beautiful job. I shall never forget the evening we applied the last touches of brilliant red and trundled our cab into the yard before our astonished mother. There stood our wagon, thirteen feet long, three and a half feet wide at the floor, from which she swelled gracefully to her full width of six feet over the wheels.

There were two hinged windows on each side and one in the back door. In the front an ingeniously arranged sliding panel gave immediate access to the driver's seat outside. We had a skillfully made set of beds which could be let down from the sides for the girls to sleep on, and under the bottom of the cab were clamped the boys' straw ticks and blankets. Every utensil which might be of use on the trip had its proper place in the built-in cupboard or on the pegs along the wall. We had built in everything the gypsies had found convenient from their centuries of such travel and had added many of our own ideas.

We knew that Mother would be angry.

"Henry!" she burst out sobbing. "What have you done?"

Father said nothing and merely kept looking at the wagon.

"You crazy old loon!" she went on yelling louder all the time. "You know you haven't the money to spend on such nonsense. You know you can't leave this farm! Why can't you be practical?"

"I've been practical all my life and I want something different for once. I've worked hard all my life and I'm going to be lazy for once," and he still looked at the wagon.

"But the neighbors, Henry! What in the world will they think to see you go down the road in that circus rig, and the turnips needing another hoeing?"

"I've wanted to go back to that little spring for forty years and all the neighbors in Canada won't stop me now!" Father looked up at her this time. Seldom indeed were the times that his will was the stronger of the two, but this was one of those rare times and she had sense enough to know it.

"There's times when I just don't know him!" she mumbled to my oldest sister, and turned into the house again with a hopeless acquiescence.

A few days later my uncle took over the duties on the farm. My mother, with the second youngest and the baby of that year, visited an aunt's a few miles away; and my father and the remaining six children set out on the greatest adventure of all time. Old Bill and the temperamental colt with which he was teamed looked at our outfit rather dubiously, and the colt shied considerably before we could get her hooked up, but once we were under way they seemed to catch the prevailing spirit and all was well.

I should have liked to have a picture of our faces when we sat inside that wagon as it rocked along the soft sod roads—six children of ages from four to seventeen, and none of us had ever been far from home. Here we were really bound for an enchanted land, a kingdom of mythical creatures who actually lived, a place which must be the most wonderful place in the world because our father wanted to go there more than anywhere else.

Everything seemed so strange and different. We saw birds such as we had never seen before. We saw new species of trees and of plants. When the horses were going slowly enough we trooped along behind the wagon and plucked the flowers that grew along the way, or chased the black squirrels along the rail fences.

Never had meals tasted so delicious as those cooked in an open fire and eaten by the side of the road. The potatoes were invariably burned, and Sister always got too much salt in the stew, but the appetites of that jolly crew noticed nothing amiss. This was the life! We did not have to think of chores, or of hoeing, or of getting back within a certain time. We were free to do exactly as we pleased. And that first day of romping and singing we covered thirty miles. We were halfway there.

That night we found it hard to go to sleep. It was different when you could look up at the stars, could hear the crickets at your elbows and the owls in the trees overhead, and were aware of the rustle and smell of new straw beneath you. It was late when fatigue got the upper hand of excitement and we sank into sleep.

Early on the morning of the third day we pulled up at our destination. We had finally reached the spring of our father's story. I was almost afraid that I would be disappointed, but I wasn't, and I think no one else was. Father said it had changed a great deal, but it was still very beautiful. Someone had built a fence about it, and some very modern and realistic Holstein cattle grazed nearby, but there were still the girlish birches fingering in the tiny silver stream as it bubbled from the cool, mysterious depths of the earth's bosom and tinkled and trickled over the red and blue granite rocks down the slope. Bowing at a respectful distance away from the magic little stream was an army of iris, yellow and blue and deep purple. Over the smooth rocks through which the rivulet had centuries ago cut its course grew moss as green as emerald and as fine as a fairy's lawn might be. And here and there were little red tufts jutting above the green just as a fairy's flowers might do.

The second day we located the crayfish, and they *were* brilliant blue with orange claws just as Father had said! Sure enough, they *did* have little clay turrets along the banks, and the biggest one *did* seem to come out to defend his kingdom. And no hunter in the most treacherous mountains of Alaska ever got more genuine satisfaction from the chase than we did in capturing our first blue crayfish.

I remember when it was all over, and we were crowded around the pan from whence our victim eyed us curiously with his bulging little beads, I felt strangely sorry that we had been able to do it. For the blue crayfish was no longer a mystical, shadowy creation of our rosy fireside fancies. He was now a fact. But he *was* blue—blue as the lowside of a rainbow.

In all, we stayed four days and we caught almost a dozen. The morning of the fifth day we reluctantly broke camp, packed our varied treasures, sealed the tank of spring water with the fabulous blue crayfish and headed homeward. And all the way home Father kept singing. He sang quietly, but he sang as we had never heard him sing before. Singing the old-time camp-meeting songs mainly . . . singing . . . singing . . . singing until the last mile of our enchanted trip was over.

It was only right that Father Kelly was one of the first to be shown the blue crayfish. And when Father showed him the safe way to hold one, he held it up and turned it to the sun as he would a flower. "What a sad, sad thing it is," he said, to himself it seemed, "that we are forever leaving the solving of the great questions to the great men!"

Chapter 16

I T W A S I N T H E '20's when the grove at Pepabun echoed to the last of its camp meetings, and ten or twelve years later the last of the faithful were finally forced to close the doors of their beloved church. But the key to those closed doors was still available to any wandering evangelist or Bible student who felt impelled to offer a sermon or two. Which meant that while there was no longer an organized congregation or a regular preacher, the church had not yet offered up the last of its hallelujahs. Its summers, in fact, were often gloriously active; and since our family had for many years now been making only the occasional pilgrimage to Pepabun, and always in the summer, its relapse into a part-time ministry did not affect us too much.

Came the war with its gas ration and soul searching, and for a time the chapel at Pepabun took on new life. Then one day with the victory won and the boys now back, the news came down to us that at long last the old building was to close its doors forever. Worse than that even, this time it would be torn down.

To Father, a close friend had been condemned to death. "Oh no!" he said, "and I was just trying to tell myself that with this here new young preacher who's been out there all summer, the old place might be raised up again!" The news was enough to put a cloud over the whole day for him. "Maybe if we'd been more faithful to it," he accused himself, "this wouldn't of happened!"

It was a Sunday evening in autumn when Father got us ready for our last trip to Pepabun. I was a schoolteacher now, and a rather outstanding one too, I thought, but I am glad now that I set aside my importance for that night and piled into the old car with the rest of the family. It was a big car, so big that, to use our Uncle George's words, "it would pass everything on the road but a gas station," but it was so full of complaint and temperament now that we were all heartily ashamed of her. And I recall that when Mother gathered her skirts and eased herself down onto her fraction of the front seat that night, she immediately gave an undignified jump and got out of the car to look at an ugly little snag the protruding spring had put in the back of her lap.

"Oh!" she fumed, "if you ever get that new car you've been promising us, Henry, I'm going to make you run this heap of old iron over the highest cliff in the country. See if I don't. The more I ride in this wreck the madder it makes me. You see if I don't."

Father helped her rub the offending spot. "Pretty soon now maybe," he said quietly. "The car's pretty hopeless all right. No arguing about that." But I could guess what he was thinking. He and Mother had been trying to build up a secret little fund for two years now for a better car, and every time they laid away another ten or twenty it seemed like the car prices leapfrogged right over the top of it every blessed time.

Well, they'd just have to get another car.

We stood in the churchyard that evening taking in the serenity of the scene, and the thought of the old place going was almost more than Father could stand. "This shouldn't be!" he said. This little old shingled shrine had meant too much to too many people!

Mother was pulling at his coat sleeve. "Let's go in," she was saying. "They'll be practicing the specials soon as the preacher comes."

So we went in and they took a back seat as they had been doing ever since they had started raising kids. A back seat made it a lot simpler when you had to lug a howling baby outside; and as Father often explained, once they had got started raising young ones, seemed as though he and Mother had never quite been able to get themselves out of the habit.

Father sat next to the open window and looked out. Late September floated with a lazy warmth over the Ontario countryside. The sun leveled off with the yellow of far fields, excited the mists of the creekbed into soft fluorescence and the breeze came up from them as fragrant and gentle as April. But there was no delirium of song in it now; just the dry scurry of the first fallen leaves—the first faint rattle of the coming death.

And I'm sure that Father, his fingers tapping idly on the sill, in his own language was thinking, "It's the same way with everything. A little light, a little life, a little time in the sun, shape for a moment and then it's all over. It's all so short. It changes so soon."

He looked at the bare fingers of the ash scratching against the upper panes as if to beg shelter from the coming frosts. He turned his eyes from the evening then and let them follow the hand-hewn rafters of the little country church up and across the calcimined ceiling. What a little while ago it was when he had first sat on one of these hard pews, his young nostrils drinking in the freshness of pine and paint, his young ears wondering at the fervor in Harry Nelson's song.

And now tomorrow or the next day or next week sometime the old chapel was to be torn down. Tomorrow she went to the highest bidder, the way they sold an old boat or war surplus or any other pile of junk which had outlived its usefulness.

Ferg McTavish, so they said, was bidding $850 for her. Might just as well have bid seven, Ferg had claimed. Nobody else wanted to be bothered with it, but then the money went to a mission fund anyhow so what did it matter if he paid a little more than was necessary?

The thought of Ferg pretending to be mission-minded and a benefactor made us cringe. We boys remembered the harvests some of us had worked for Ferg. That man was so tight you couldn't drive a flaxseed into him with a sledge hammer, we said. Fed his kids skim milk on their porridge so there would be more cream for the can. The plain fact was that Ferg was building a henhouse, a whopper of a henhouse, and he needed timbers and lumber; and he was chairman of the trustee board and the other trustees both owed him money.

"Not that I'm so religious," Father was murmuring to Mother, "but the people who built this, the people that's lying out there in the yard right now, they went without underwear and vittles to build this here church! Charlie

Stuckey gave the steer we were going to butcher for our beef that year and we ate rabbit all winter. Rabbit full of cedar!"

Oh, well, what was the use? Why get his blood pressure up ten points when there was nothing he could do about it anyhow? Things change and there always has to be an end, so why try to buck it?

Outside, the yard was beginning to fill with voices now and a few of the older people came in to get seats where they could be sure to hear well. Mother went up to visit with some of them; but though Father knew them all, he only nodded. He was in no mood to talk. And as I watched him sitting beside the window which looked over to the old camp-meeting grove, I thought I could guess what was in his mind:

Sometimes I just don't understand what's got into folks nowadays. They don't act like they used to. Time was when his neighborhood meant something to a man, and when somebody in the section needed a little help, the rest of you all ganged together in some kind of bee or other and you all put your shoulders to the wheel to help. Had fun at it too. But it's different now. People are all getting so blasted businesslike. Everybody for himself. Well, I guess that's the reason they've got the money for all these here combines and milking machines and electric fences and movable gutters and whatnot. That's the way they get the money to buy up old churches too.

Eight hundred and fifty dollars. Henhouse! Going to guillotine its steeple and smash in its eyes and strip off its skin and knock its very bones apart to build a henhouse!

Father shook his head. To him this dismantling of the church must have seemed like taking a wrecking bar to the Ark of the Covenant.

There was the noise of a tired motor outside, the slamming of car doors, and then the preacher came in with his wife and his music cases. "Why, hello, Henry. Hello, Mrs. Green." Mr. Gillespie dropped his guitar case and shook hands. His wife came over too, smiled and went on to the front.

"Pretty fair, Reverend. How's yourself? Giving us something a little special for tonight? Kind of hard to think of it being the last service, isn't it?"

The younger man became sober and rubbed his brown fingers along the back of the pew. "I've been sort of hoping and praying that we'd find some way to keep the old place open," he said quietly. "But there just doesn't seem to be any way out. It's not the Lord's will, I guess. I'm afraid it's going to seem a bit like a funeral tonight, Henry. Well, I've got to go. I see the wife has her guitar out already."

He was a likable young fellow, Father thought. Just a kid and not too smart maybe. Did all his Bible study out of a correspondence school with no particular church behind him. Never could be ordained. Not the regular run of clergy at all. That's why the trustees always called him a preacher instead of a minister and mister instead of reverend. Gillespie was just an ordinary man who did ordinary work and preached when he could. Hired out anywhere he could make an honest dollar. Pitched sheaves. Dug postholes.

"But sometimes," Father used to say, "I think that's the kind of man I like best to listen to. Now you take these long-robed fellows with the pink faces and the pretty hands you see in the town churches—what have they got to say to a man like me? One of them gives a sermon on swearing, for instance. Would an ordinary lunkhead of a working man be swallowing it whole? More likely he'd be saying, 'And what does the likes of you know about wanting to swear? Ever get your pants full of barley awns, Reverend? Bull ever step on your bunion?' But a man can't talk back like that to a guy like Gillespie.

"Of course now maybe his preaching might be a little off the beam. I'm no one to argue about that; but what would it matter anyway? Nobody's got a mortgage on all the truth. But here's a lad that's burning up with something to say and willing to go through fire and storm to say it, and right or wrong by the eternal, I think he ought to have the chance to say it!"

"Full of the spirit!" Harry Nelson would have said.

From the front came a sudden burst of music. The couple were practicing a duet. She was singing the alto and he was carrying the air. Both strummed guitars. There was something about the woman that must have reminded Father of the way our mother used to look when she sang up there on that same platform in the days when she was still young and the church still smelled of its newness. No lipstick, no jewelry, hair in a bun. And something about the eyes too: always looking up and beyond.

Cars began to putter into the yard outside; the puttering was mixed with the rumble of buggy tires and the heavy clatter of horse feet. Oh, there were a few of the old kind left. The gogetters hadn't crowded them all out yet. That buggy with the shaky steel tires would be Janie McGill's— Janie, who looked after her sick husband and the three grandkids their girls had sent home and who still found time to milk the cows and feed the pigs and swing the scythe. Seventy-two, Janie must be now, but she never missed a Sunday. The only time in the week she ever sat down.

"And now why in the world didn't Ferg give her a ride in that new sedan of his instead of letting her drive that three miles with the old Clyde?" Father murmured to me. "He went right by the place!"

The church began to fill. The singing stopped and the preacher sat down in a front seat to give his notes a last scanning. And now a steady stream of people filed down the aisles. Some came in with their heads held high, their eyes challenging, marching like the good Christian soldiers they professed to be to their front seats. To the very front marched Ferg McTavish, giving restrained little smiles in all directions, bowing correctly and reverently as he took his place, even moving his lips in a prayer as he sat down.

And some came in like old Job Barlow and Janie Mc-Gill, on tiptoes, guilty-eyed, bowed humble by what the section knew of them. Old Job crept into the seat just ahead of us and cautiously nodded. The stain of a recent quid was still brown on his chin.

"Big crowd," Job whispered.

"Last service," Mother replied brightly.

"Last time I'll ever be going to any church, I reckon, 'cept when they carry me in. I'd feel like a bug under a spyglass anywhere else. . . ."

Mother smiled back for an answer, but Father didn't.

"This shouldn't be!" he said to me.

The preacher's voice cut through the rustling. This service was not to be a mournful one, he said. True, he like many more of them would be sad to see the old church go. The section just wouldn't seem the same somehow. But the trustees had considered the question thoughtfully and prayerfully and the Lord had led them to decide other-wise. Who were we to question or to mourn the Almighty's will? We should rejoice in it. Something better must surely lie ahead for us.

The preacher started the hymns, his hand cutting the air into triangles, his head shaking with the glory of it. They sang the hymns which everyone knew: "When the Roll Is Called," "Old One Hundred," "Holy, Holy," "The Glory Song"; and when the preacher could think of no more he called for requests.

Father seemed surprised when Mother called for "Rock of Ages." She had never really been the kind to make much fuss over religion, even when the skies were darkest. When things got so rough that another woman might have wanted to call a prayer meeting, Mother was more apt to feel like shaking her fists or kicking someone in the shins or giving someone a hot piece of her mind. But sometimes when the storms had broken, when the last hope had to be abandoned and when too much of pain or sorrow had finally quelled her quick-tempered heart, she might sing to herself. And the song she usually chose was "Rock of Ages." It was the one she had requested for her father's funeral. It was the one she had hummed the time she was walking the floor in her first labor when she should have been in bed yelling her head off. It was the one she had asked us to sing for her when her time came.

Father had always liked it too, and I think now that his love for that hymn came from its assurance that one thing in this changing world would always be the same. He couldn't understand the reason for change. He hated it. I recall one Sunday evening after they came back from this Pepabun church and after the children were all in bed and when there was nothing to hear but the fiddling of the crickets, Father said, "Lots of changes since you and I started out, Jean. Too many of them. And nothing's the

same with us any more, Jean, only that little church where
you and I used to make eyes on camp-meeting Sundays,
where you marched me down the aisle to marry me, where
we watched our first youngsters say their first recitations
come Christmas time. I'm glad it's the same, Jean."

The hymn died away. Mother settled back in her seat.
The preacher declared the meeting open for testimony.

"I think that we shall make our testimonies short tonight," he suggested, "because there will no doubt be
many who would like to pay a farewell tribute to this little
chapel our fathers hewed out of the wilderness. Many will
no doubt wish to tell us tonight of the blessing it has been
in their lives."

There was a short wait for the first response, and then
people jumped up all over the place. Some merely quoted
a text. Some labored on and on till the preacher politely
eased them into silence and gave the floor to someone else.
Some whispered. Some started a chorus.

We knew that it would soon be time for Ferg McTavish.
Ferg always waited till the rabble had finished with its
cruder orations. Ferg's speech always ended the testimony
part, and you had to admit it, he was a good speaker. He
knew when to pause, when to shout, when to whisper. He
could be discreetly humorous. He didn't look out of the
window or down at his toes; he turned to look his hearers
square in the face.

Ferg was just as sorry as anyone about closing the
church, he said. His father and mother had sacrificed much
from their very little to build this place. And he personally
owed more to the church than he could ever repay. But
there comes a time when emotion must give way to common sense, he said. Times had changed. People didn't
need a little old chapel stuck up on every side road now as

they used to. The car had changed that. A mile was only a minute today.

Father looked across at Janie, saw her face redden. Blast it all, he was thinking, how could Ferg say such a thing and keep his face straight!

". . . What is the sense of trying to keep open a little chapel like this which can't afford an ordained pastor—a church which doesn't even have a name? Now just six miles away, downtown in Grand Valley or up in Arthur, there are lots of churches, copyrighted varieties, pastors with degrees and pedigrees, take your pick, lots of room in any of them. . . ."

"And what would happen to folks like old Job or Janie down there?" Father asked me in a bitter whisper.

The preacher didn't hurry Ferg and Ferg took all the time he needed to be dramatic. And when he had finished Mr. Gillespie picked up his Bible to read the text as he always did before the collection. He didn't see Janie on her feet until his wife pulled his sleeve. He closed his Bible then and waited.

We waited too, surprised. Janie had never testified before in all her life. Testifying was something you left to those who professed.

But Janie didn't say anything. She stood there for a moment, her pinched face burning red against the cheap purple of her hat, her big knuckles restless and white.

"Go ahead, Janie," the preacher said softly. "We'd be glad to hear from you."

The woman's lips moved, groping for words. But the words couldn't be found. The big worn hands suddenly flew to her face. Janie burst into sobs and sat down. The sobs kept on. In all the place there was no other sound.

The preacher wasn't quite sure what to say at first.

When he partially recovered, he said, "Never mind, Janie. The deepest things are often too deep for words." And then after he had thought more carefully, "But—but it's folk like you who make me want to be a preacher, Janie." There was a curious rise in Mr. Gillespie's voice and we all wondered whether he was going to make it.

"Bawling women always did make a fool out of me!" Father muttered as he stirred uncomfortably.

The preacher read the text. Then they started the "special" which always came just before the collection. Something about the Home over there, the song was.

Mr. Gillespie stopped between verses to exhort a little. "Many feel just like Janie did tonight, knowing that this is the last time we shall ever meet together in this humble house of worship. Many of us will feel lost, homeless. But I want to tell you that one day there's going to be a great reunion, over there, beyond the river, in that Home that shall stand forever, in that Mansion the Master has gone to prepare for us. . . . Oh yes, we try to build our fine homes here; and we try to fill them and surround them with trinkets and gadgets and a thousand things to tickle our fancy and make life easy. But of worldly possessions the Good Book says that the rust will canker and the moth will eat. . . . No, friends, this earth is not our home; we're just apassing through."

And then Mr. Gillespie blew his nose and nodded to his wife and they began singing again of the Home over there.

When the song ended Janie started to cry again, only she wasn't alone now. Mother was sniffing too and she was just about the last woman in the world to carry on. The ushers tried not to notice and went up to the front for the collection plates as sedately as ever.

When Father leaned over toward her I thought it was to

offer her some secret sympathy, but I was mistaken. There was nothing soothing in his words at all. "Jean!" he asked in an impatient rumble, "is the checkbook in your purse?"

"Why?"

"I could write a check on the car money," he said. "Nine hundred would do."

She handed him the checkbook, but the look she gave him as she did so almost led him to give it back again. It was a curious, persistent staring that she gave him, and he couldn't figure it out. He couldn't tell whether she was itching to strangle him or whether she just wanted to put her arms around him. He had little time to wonder. Quickly, he tore a blank leaf from a hymnbook and wrote:

"Dear Reverend, take this here check and buy us the church in the morning. Please."

Then he folded the note in with the check, made them into a tight little ball that the ushers wouldn't see till later, and when the plate came around to him, he tossed it in.

As soon as the service was over, Father got us away in a hurry. He didn't want to be around when the ushers counted out the money. And all the way home he kept glancing across at Mother, kept wondering what she was going to say to him. Mother was a hard one to figure out sometimes, and when she decided to lay into a man she sure could do a proper job of it. And she'd often done it for far less foolishness than this.

For a full five minutes Father waited for her to open up, but not a word came out of her and her face was harder to read than ever. The suspense was telling on his nerves, and finally he tried to start a little conversation.

"Old car's perking along pretty good lately," he said.

"Oh?"

He waited for another half mile. "A good overhauling and a paint job might make a real car out of her maybe."

She didn't even say oh to that, and Father didn't feel like coaxing the talk any farther. Well, why didn't she let him have it then?

They turned into the lane. The old car panted and hobbled along the stony ruts, and finally, with a cough and a rheumatic jerk, pulled up at the back-yard gate. Mother dismounted and turned halfway round on herself to look at another snag on the back of her dress.

"I'm going to upholster that seat first thing in the morning," she said. "See if I don't. I'll cover up that old spring if I have to empty a whole bushel of wool on it. See if I don't!"

And when Father looked at her this time, she could hold it no longer, and she took his hand and broke into such a fit of laughing that the dogs came piling out the back door to see what in the world was wrong.

And he knew then that nothing was wrong. Nothing in the world.

Chapter 17

So, Father, it's time to get ready for another Thanksgiving and another family reunion. Once again your sons and daughters will collect from all over the country and surround you and Mother with the squalling of our babes, the giggling of our teen-agers and the not too subtle boasting of ourselves who should be old enough to know better.

I feel a bit apprehensive already. You would be the last to admit it, of course, but you are now somewhat past that age when you could sit in a room shivering with bedlam and not be wearied. After all, you're long past that three-score and ten you used to read about in the Scripture which always used to end our day back on the farm. Fourteen years past it.

I've been trying to shake that thought for quite a while now. Sure, I know how we joked with you last year about how much younger you were than your years. Our little daddy was still tougher than a buzzard's gizzard, someone said. And when we left, our farewells were full of bright talk about how soon we would all see you again. We didn't even bother to join hands at the last and sing our usual "God Be With You Till We Meet Again."

And you played the game with us. As we were bundling into the car for the trip back home, you merely reminded me to express you that piece of organ mahogany I had told you about. "I'll have you a sewing cabinet next time you come," you promised.

We were all too carefully casual. We had seen the signs: the nap you had to take each afternoon; the little box of heart pills on your bureau; the worry in Mother's face whenever you climbed the stairs. Things which all seemed so new, so strange to you!

I know that I can write all this without frightening you—that you may even smile, for God can know but few men so ready. And we all know too that if you are careful, you may be spared for many a year yet, which is the possibility we are all so eager to talk about. I write this now because I realize that other possibility. And that constant shying away from emotion, which you yourself instilled in us all, has kept me too long from saying too many things which have a right to be said.

Besides, it's a time for giving thanks.

First, let me say thanks now for the home that was ours. I'm afraid sometimes that you're rather ashamed of what you had to give us—the half-starved farm with the sagging, moss-eaten barns, the house that you were always going to enlarge, the floor with the pine knots which were always stabbing holes through the linoleum, and the cast-iron range with the crack which let the smoke into the oven. I wish you wouldn't worry about such things. They didn't matter.

Yes, I remember how cold those unheated bedrooms could be with a zero wind forcing the winter's morning through the rag-lined cracks about the windows. But I remember more clearly the way you would quietly come back up the stairs after you had the fire roaring in the kitchen below, and pile our clothes about the stovepipe so they wouldn't be so frigid when we had to climb into them. I remember the straw-filled ticks too, and how they were forever rustling as if the rats were still in them. How they would roll one onto the floor when they were new, and into a valley full of knolls when they were broken in. But I'll remember longer how we used to wake up some night with a new storm howling down the pipe to find that you had been in already to add your mackinaw or your old coon coat to the too-scanty weight of our blankets.

I haven't forgotten the work we had to do either. How bitterly we used to complain on a May afternoon when the other boys could stay after school for ball practice and we had to hurry home to milk or to clean out the pigpens. I haven't forgotten how it used to feel on a powder-dusty day in July when we would look up from the sweat and thistles of a hayfield and see the other youngsters go singing up the side road to the swimming pool. I haven't forgotten the crippling drudgery of picking up potatoes on a crisp September Saturday when our team needed us for a game of rugby or lacrosse down at the fairgrounds. I haven't forgotten threshing day, with our shoes full of barley awns, our eyes shut with chaff and our lungs so clogged with smut that we could spit mud.

But you must believe me now when I say that even for

those long, long hours of work, I can find no accusation in me. Maybe that is because I can never forget the way Thanksgiving used to be at our house.

Thanksgiving was the day when we took stock of what all this labor had brought us. You always managed to organize a little procession for that day. First we went to the cellar with its barrels of apples whose fragrance seeped up into the kitchen as soon as we opened the door, the bins of beets and carrots packed in sand, the cabbages and onions hanging from the beam, the sheaves of celery, the mountain of sacked potatoes and turnips.

You had us inventory it all carefully, the number of pounds, of bushels, of bunches. Finally we classified and counted the preserves which bowed down the shelves in the corner next the cistern: peas, corn, string beans, lima beans, wax beans, jellies of a dozen colors, rhubarb, rhubarb with pineapple, rhubarb with strawberries, strawberries without rhubarb, wild strawberries. . . . The list seems endless now.

Then we went out to the barns, and from the tables on the backs of our scribblers, we figured the tons of hay which we had stowed away in the gaunt belly of the mow, the bushels of oats, wheat and barley in our granary. We counted the lazy, grunting livestock, the hens, the geese.

You wanted to see how we stood, you said, to see how we compared with last year, for instance. Or with that year—it was '24—when we had set a record. And maybe you did. But I think that you wanted most for us to realize, on this feast day, how richly the Almighty had smiled upon all those hours of work that we had so tearfully protested. And when we finally sat down to the feast which Mother and the girls had prepared for us, the grace for which we bowed our heads was something which we felt.

But you may think it strange for me to say now that the Thanksgiving I shall always remember most thankfully was the one when it seemed we had nothing to be thankful for.

For our house, at least, the wet year started off with more promise than most. We had hay left over that year, we had lots of seed and our four litters of piglets were as sleek as sausages. What was more, you had a little money set aside, for that was the year you thought we might finally afford a hayloader.

Ever since we could remember, for one parch-throated summer after another, every bundle we had built onto a load had been lifted with a last-ounce straining of your own sweating back. You left the easier job of building the load to us boys. Some of your neighbors used to laugh at you for that. "Build a good back on them while they're young," they used to tell you. "Comes in handy later."

You went on pitching. Our day would come soon enough, you said.

But now you had enough money put aside to buy us a hayloader, a wonderful machine that simply trailed behind the wagon, lifted the stubborn windrows clear and threw them on the rack at your feet.

I think we must have sent to every implement company in Canada for circulars that spring.

Then the hydro came. Not to us, of course, but into the houses around which were fine enough to receive it. The MacKillops had a little party one night after it went into their home and we went. We marveled at the white bright rooms, the toaster, the iron that no longer had to sit on the stove, the little motor in the cellar that sucked water from the well outside and sent it gushing to the kitchen sink and all the way upstairs to the new bathroom. And Mother looked a long time at the washing machine.

Outside afterward, there were the usual doubts. Angus Smith thought that extravagance like that might be the ruination of a good farmer, and Einar Neilsen, who was always concerned with what this world was coming to, wondered cautiously if all this new power might not be just a little too worldly.

Whatever its iniquities, we knew that electricity had come to stay, and every day we heard the singing in the wires that went over our gate; we felt its challenge. If only we could afford to be connected!

I'm sure it was a Monday when we found out what was in your mind. I know it was a Monday because Mother was doing her big wash that night, and you left us floundering with our homework to go over and help her.

"This here diaper steam might be good for what ails a man," you said. "My turn now."

And Mother protested as she always did. The kids wanted you to read to them, she said. But you shoved her aside and took over the board. "Might be the Lord's will for you to have a houseful of urchins," you said, "but He sure can't be expecting you to do all this scrubbing for them."

Mother took up her knitting then, pulling her chair in as close to the lamp on the kitchen table as she could.

"Washing and knitting. Knitting and washing. You spend more time doing that than you do sleeping, don't you, Jean?"

Mother declared that she ruined a washboard a year.

"Think we ought to break down and get this here electricity?" you asked.

Mother's knitting fell into her lap.

You said, "I don't like seeing you ruin so many wash-boards—nor your eyes either. . . . And if I cut my own poles, I think maybe the hayloader money would just about pay for it. . . ."

Mother came flying across the room and threw her arms about your neck and I think she swallowed a tear or two. Then she sobered as she thought about the hayloader that wouldn't be bought now. "You're not as young as you used to be," she said.

But you thought that your rheumatism could surely wait for another year.

So the hydro came up our lane too one day. The hay-loader money didn't allow for anything fancy—nothing like the MacKillop's. But what wonder there was to that gleaming washing machine and to that solitary, yellow-veined bulb which dangled naked from each of our ceil-ings! And what a banquet splendor there was now to a supper eaten in this unbelievable brilliance!

Sometimes when we could sneak off to one of the other rooms, we youngsters would play with the switch by the hour just to see the marvel of it over and over.

No more lamps to fill. No more wicks to dehorn. No more sooty chimneys to dirty the dishwater. The lamps went quietly off to the attic one day. All of them. Even the one we had been so proud of—the special one with the frosted bowl and the bunch of red grapes.

The coming of the hydro was almost the last good thing that the year was to bring us. The rains started just as the first oat spears began to stab through the earth and when their growth put a pea-green haze over the whole countryside. When the water finally drained away again, there wasn't a seeding anywhere which had survived.

Those who had the extra seed or the extra money seeded again and hoped desperately that the rest of the year would be kinder, that the weather would be lenient enough to let them harvest before the frosts came.

But September only brought back the rains. The few crops which were cut early enough sprouted in the stooks, and most of the grain was never cut. Most of it merely lay down and let the incessant rain beat it back into the earth. There was a man up the road, whose name I have forgotten now, who went out of his head that year and went raving out into his fields one night with a lantern and scythe.

There wasn't even a healthy potato that year. They rotted in the mud.

And I remember one day when everybody was down at the store comparing miseries, Angus Smith reminded those to whom the shoe fit that maybe they could see now why he had warned against putting so much money into the extravagance of electricity instead of leaving it in the bank for a rainy day. And Einar Neilsen wondered if maybe it wasn't the electricity itself which was doing something wicked to the air.

You sold a couple of cows that fall, and all of our pigs and a lot of other livestock you had really intended to keep. You had to take heartbreaking prices for them because everybody else around was doing the same thing. But you got enough to buy flour and oatmeal and a few potatoes, and you managed to pay the interest.

About all that we had to harvest that fall was a field of turnips which had somehow weathered the wet, and one

Saturday when the first sleet was bouncing along the furrow, we dug them and carried them into the cellar.

And then suddenly, as if it had crept upon us like a dog we had forgotten to lock behind, it was Thanksgiving time again.

"Maybe we better forget it this year," Mother said. "Can't make much of a feast out of turnips. We haven't even left ourselves a goose."

But the night before the big day you set a trap out by the haystack, and in the morning you brought in a jack-rabbit. "These aren't half bad sometimes if you roast them with a hunk of fat pork," you said. "Let's try it."

And grudgingly, screwing up her face with distaste, Mother started the job. "But it's going to be a good long time before a tough old thing like that will be cooked," she promised. "Don't expect to eat till it's good and late."

We took inventory as usual that year, and you did your best to be cheerful. "We'll make out all right," you kept saying.

But I'm afraid that Mother had already spoken the mood that was in all of us, and all we could think of was the things that we weren't going to be able to have now: the new shoes, the new coats, the toboggan, the skates and hockey sticks and all the dozen and one other things which we had so carefully selected from the new catalogue.

And then, late that night when we finally sat down to the jackrabbit, someone said, "It looks like a piece of old dead horse! I don't want any!"

And Mother cried.

You pretended that it wasn't serious. "It hasn't been such a bad year really, Jean?" you said. And then just when we thought you were about to sit down to say grace, you did a strange thing. You went up to the attic and got the lamp with the bunch of red grapes. You lighted it, set it in the middle of the table and told one of us to turn out the lights.

"A real feast is supposed to have candlelight," you explained, "but a lamp should do just as well."

And when there was only the lamp again, we couldn't believe our eyes. Could it really have been this dark before? Surely not! The chimney must be dirty or maybe the wick was plugged! Why, how in the world did we ever see our way around in those days?

You waited till we were quiet, and then you said the awkward grace which you always composed for such a special day. When you were finished, we were still strangely quiet.

In the humble insufficiency of the old lamp, we were beginning to see clearly again. "That's right," Mother said. "A year ago we *had* to have this!"

It got to be a lovely meal. The jackrabbit tasted like turkey. Better than turkey. And the turnips were the mildest we could ever recall.

No wonder Mother has kept that little frosted lamp all through the years. I saw it in her bedroom last time I was down.

Thank you for that Thanksgiving, Father. For that and all the other Thanksgivings we had with you. And for the home that, for all its want, was so rich for us all.

That's what I wanted to say in this letter.

And now your sons and daughters are eagerly getting ready to descend upon you for the reunion of yet another Thanksgiving. We will come doing our foolish best to display the success which has come to our several ways. We all have so many, many bright things now, and we'll not be content until you hear all about them.

But, Father, when it's time for the feast itself, and before we bow for the grace you will compose, would you bring out that old oil lamp again? Switch out all the rest and let it light our feast again?

Maybe we need its humble gleam as badly in these great days of our noisy success as we did in that year of our poverty.